File Folder FAMILY HOME E

New Testament

Show-and-Tell Presentations and Activities with Memorable Thought Treats

12 New Testament Themes:

HEAVENLY TREASURES: Follow the Straight and Narrow Path

SEEDS OF FAITH: My Testimony Is Growing

ANGEL TELLS OF TWO BIRTHS: John and Jesus

LET'S CELEBRATE the Birth of Jesus

CREATING ME: I'm Trying to Be Like Jesus

FISHERS OF MEN: Jesus Chose 12 Apostles

BLESSED BEATITUDES: Jesus Gave the Sermon on the Mount

THE GIFTS HE GAVE: Tell Me the Stories of Jesus

SERVICE WITH A SMILE: Jesus Performed Miracles

CHOOSE THE RIGHT: Jesus Is Our Light

CAPTAIN OF OUR SHIP: Jesus Is Our Life Savior

IN HIS STEPS: Spotlighting the Life of Jesus

Covenant Communications, Inc.
American Fork, Utah

Printed in the United States of America
First Printing: August 1998

File Folder FAMILY HOME EVENINGS - New Testament

ISBN 1-57734-297-6

INTRODUCTION

With these *File Folder FAMILY HOME EVENINGS* you can teach children about the New Testament in a fun way, helping them gain a testimony of Jesus.

These file-folder-size show-and-tell presentations and activities allow you to create a family home evening in minutes, then file the activities away to use again and again. You can also use the same size visuals for Primary and Sunday School lessons. Enlarge visuals for Primary talks and sharing time presentations.

Children ages 6 and older enjoy presenting and participating. Plus, Thought Treats increase their appetite for more learning.

Simply photocopy the patterns, color and cut them out, and place them in a file folder with tape or sticky-back Velcro. You'll find file folder labels on page iii to help you organize.

> **HEAVENLY TREASURES:**
> Follow the Straight and Narrow Path
>
> *File Folder Family Home Evenings*
> *NEW TESTAMENT*

STEPS TO FAMILY HOME EVENING (1 Nephi 17:15):

1. MUSIC: Sing the suggested song from the *Children's Songbook** and have an opening prayer.
2. SCRIPTURE and INTRODUCTION: Read a scripture (one found in the lesson cue cards), and then read the introduction for each family home evening theme.
3. LESSON: Place the show-and-tell visuals inside the file folder as you read the cue cards. Use Velcro or tape to attach visuals.
4. ACTIVITY: Enjoy a game or activity (storing patterns inside a separate folder).
5. TREAT: Have the closing prayer with a blessing on the food, then top the evening off with a Thought Treat (recipes on introduction pages and on pages 111-118).

Week after week, children and parents will look forward to being together as you learn and share stories from the Bible. Children will better remember lessons they help to teach. Their self-esteem increases as they give these Show-and-Tell presentations and activities.

PRIMARY TEACHERS AND LEADERS: Primary teachers, you can add presentations, activities, and treats to support your New Testament lessons. Delegate to your class by cutting out and distributing cue cards and visuals. The presentations and activities are ideal for Primary Sharing Time (enlarging visuals for a large group).

MORE LESSON HELP: See *PRIMARY PARTNERS: New Testament (manual 7)* with activities to match each lesson #1-46 (also by Ross and Guymon-King).

We suggest you present these family home evenings in the order they appear in this book, as each theme portrays the stages of Jesus' life with the exception of "In His Steps: Spotlighting the Life of Jesus." For Sharing Time, use presentations when they fit the monthly theme. For classroom, choose themes that fit the lessons.

HOW TO ORGANIZE: (1) Assign tasks using the "Buzz on Over for Family Home Evening" chart (shown left—patterns and instructions on pages ii and iv). Place bees (with family names) in chart pockets to delegate family home evening assignments.
(2) Color and cut out patterns and instructions ahead of time, giving each person their part. (3) Purchase and prepare Thought Treats.
(4) Purchase supplies: File folders, crayons or markers, tape or Velcro, and balloons (see Create Me: I'm Trying to Be Like Jesus theme). (5) Enjoy!

> **COPYRIGHT NOTICE:** Patterns in this book are for use by individual families only. Copying patterns for any other use is prohibited.

LOOK FOR THIS BOOK ON CD-ROM.

Children's Songbook is published by The Church of Jesus Christ of Latter-day Saints, Salt Lake City, Utah.

File Folder FAMILY HOME EVENINGS - New Testament
PATTERN: Buzz on Over for Family Home Evening! Assignment Chart
Write family names in wings, cut slits in hive.
Laminate bees and hive. Cut slits in hive and insert bees.
Glue mount on paper on hive edges 1/4" leaving pockets open.

PATTERN: *Labels for File Folders:* Create two separate file folders for each theme. Copy one set of labels to place on the Show-and-Tell presentation folders, and a second set of labels to place on the game or activity file folder. Place other labels on file folders to help you organize family activities and thought treats.

HEAVENLY TREASURES:
Follow the Straight and Narrow Path

File Folder Family Home Evenings
NEW TESTAMENT

SEEDS OF FAITH:
My Testimony Is Growing

File Folder Family Home Evenings
NEW TESTAMENT

ANGEL TELLS OF TWO BIRTHS:
John and Jesus

File Folder Family Home Evenings
NEW TESTAMENT

LET'S CELEBRATE
the Birth of Jesus

File Folder Family Home Evenings
NEW TESTAMENT

CREATING ME:
I'm Trying to Be Like Jesus

File Folder Family Home Evenings
NEW TESTAMENT

FISHERS OF MEN:
Jesus Chose 12 Apostles

File Folder Family Home Evenings
NEW TESTAMENT

BLESSED BEATITUDES:
Jesus Gave the Sermon on the Mount

File Folder Family Home Evenings
NEW TESTAMENT

THE GIFTS HE GAVE:
Tell Me the Stories of Jesus

File Folder Family Home Evenings
NEW TESTAMENT

SERVICE WITH A SMILE:
Jesus Performed Miracles

File Folder Family Home Evenings
NEW TESTAMENT

CHOOSE THE RIGHT:
Jesus Is Our Light

File Folder Family Home Evenings
NEW TESTAMENT

CAPTAIN OF OUR SHIP:
Jesus Is Our Life Savior

File Folder Family Home Evenings
NEW TESTAMENT

IN HIS STEPS:
Spotlighting the Life of Jesus

File Folder Family Home Evenings
NEW TESTAMENT

FAMILY HOME EVENING LESSON AND ACTIVITY PLANS

FAMILY HOME EVENING THOUGHT TREATS

FAMILY FUN ACTIVITIES:
Sports, Games, Plays, Musical Entertainment

FAMILY DAILY DEVOTIONALS:
Scripture, *Ensign*, *Era*, and *Friend* Reading

FAMILY COUNSEL:
Interviews and Goal Setting

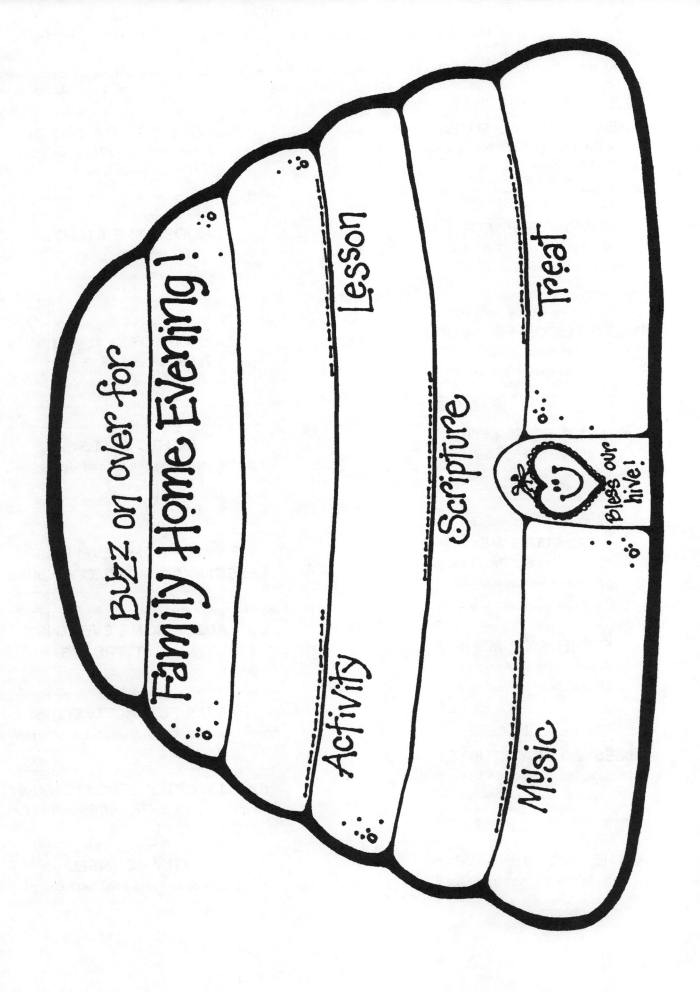

File Folder *FAMILY HOME EVENINGS*
New Testament
TABLE OF CONTENTS

TABLE OF CONTENTS

Pages:

File Folder FAMILY HOME EVENING

HEAVENLY TREASURES: Follow the Straight and Narrow Path

OPENING SONG: "I Will Follow God's Plan," page164 in the *Children's Songbook**.

INTRODUCTION:

Tell family, "Let's learn how to follow the straight and narrow path that leads to heaven. In this family home evening you will discover that you are HEAVEN SENT and HEAVEN BOUND."

"Lay not up for yourselves treasures upon earth, ... But ... treasures in heaven" (Matthew 6:19-21).

Don't leave this life empty-handed. Choose treasures that are of lasting worth. DIG DEEP into the scriptures to find heavenly treasures.

HEAVENLY TREASURES:
Follow the Straight Path
FILE FOLDER
SHOW-AND-TELL:

CREATE: Cut out cue cards (pages 2-3) and file folder label (page iii). Color and cut out visuals (pages 4-5). Glue the label on file folder.

PRESENT: Read cue cards and place visuals on folder with tape or Velcro.

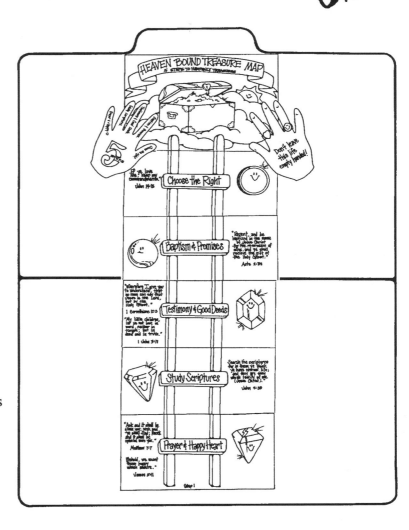

ACTIVITY: Jewels of Thought Spin the Bottle game. See page 6 for details.

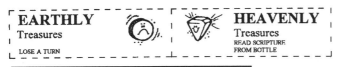

EARTHLY
Treasures

LOSE A TURN

HEAVENLY
Treasures
READ SCRIPTURE
FROM BOTTLE

STRAIT GATE: "Strive to enter in at the strait gate: for many, I say unto you, will seek to enter in, and shall not be able." (Luke 13:24)

THOUGHT TREAT: <u>Heaven Sent, Heaven Bound Milk Shake</u>. See page 111 for details.

---

*Children's Songbook is published by The Church of Jesus Christ of Latter-day Saints, Salt Lake City, Utah.

FILE FOLDER SHOW-AND-TELL:

#1   HEAVENLY TREASURES: Follow the Straight and Narrow Path

We are HEAVEN SENT and HEAVEN BOUND. Before we were born, we lived in heaven. After we die, we can return to live with Heavenly Father.

When we die, we can <u>not</u> take things money can buy, like a bike, racing wheels, or gold watch, with us. So, **DON'T LEAVE THIS LIFE EMPTY-HANDED.**

Take HEAVENLY TREASURES. These are treasures of lasting worth, for example: Prayer and a happy heart, scripture study, testimony and good deeds, baptism and promises, and choosing the right.

#2

To get to heaven, follow the straight and narrow path. Come, let's climb the ladder.

STEP #1 is PRAYER:
♥ Pray to talk to Heavenly Father.
♥ Prayer helps you have a happy heart.

<u>HOW DO YOU PRAY? SAY</u>:
○ Father in Heaven: ○ I thank thee for my many blessings.
○ Please bless those in need.
○ In the name of Jesus Christ, Amen.

<u>WHEN DO YOU PRAY?</u>
Pray morning and night to keep heaven in sight.

#3   Step #2 is Study the Scriptures.

♥ The New Testament and other scriptures tell about Jesus.
♥ Jesus is Heavenly Father's Son. He came to earth to teach us about God's plan.
♥ The scriptures tell us how to get to heaven.

You can stay on the straight and narrow path that leads to heaven by reading the scriptures each day.

FILE FOLDER SHOW-AND-TELL:

#4

Step #3 is Testimony and Good Deeds.

We can gain a testimony that Jesus Christ is the Son of God by reading the New Testament and other scriptures.

We can know that Jesus lived, and that he taught the people about our Heavenly Father's plan for us. How can you know? By reading the scriptures and praying about what you have read. A special feeling from the Holy Ghost will come into your heart.

Our testimony is a special light. Share that light by doing good deeds. Do as Jesus would do. Walk in his steps. We can learn to love and care for others as he did.

#5

Step #4 is Baptism.

Jesus showed us the way to heaven when he was baptized by immersion. Immersion means to go completely under the water to bury your sins. Jesus did not have any sins. He was perfect. But he was baptized to show us the way.

Jesus wants us to become perfect like he is. He wants us to live the commandments each day, so that one day we can live with him and with Heavenly Father again.

When we are baptized, we make promises to obey the commandments. If we do wrong, we need to ask Heavenly Father to forgive us, and we promise not to do that wrong again.

#6

Step #5 is Choose the Right.

♥ Good choices make us happy,
   and bad choices make us sad.
♥ Let's choose to obey Heavenly
   Father's commandments, and we
   will be happy.

Let's GO FOR THE HEAVENLY GOLD:
A golden testimony is the best kind of gold, because we can take it with us to heaven. So, let's make golden choices and choose golden friends.

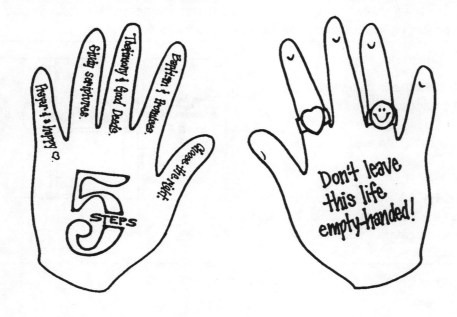

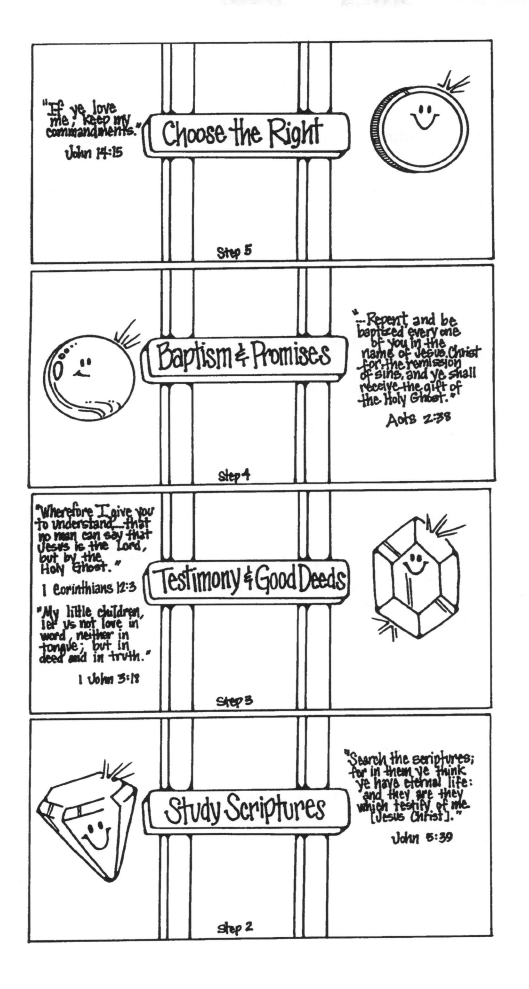

ACTIVITY: Jewels of Thought Spin the Bottle

OBJECTIVE: Learn that the scriptures are Jewels of Thought--messages of great worth and value.

TO MAKE GAME AND PRIZES: (1) Color and cut out bottle and lid labels (page 7) and glue on bottle and bottle lid. (2) Cut out scripture strips, fold, and place in bottle. (3) Cut out prize glue-on stickers (below and page 11) and place in a container to draw from. (4) Cut out Earthly and Heavenly Treasures wordstrips (pages 8-9).

EARTHLY Treasures — LOSE A TURN

HEAVENLY Treasures — READ SCRIPTURE FROM BOTTLE

HOW TO PLAY: (1) Players sit in a circle and place the Earthly and Heavenly Treasures wordstrip (page 10, shown left) in front of them. (2) A player starts by spinning the bottle. (3) When the bottle stops in front of a player, look to see if bottle neck is pointing to Earthly Treasures to lose a turn, or Heavenly Treasures to draw a scripture strip from the bottle and read aloud. Don't place the scripture back in the bottle. (4) Player who reads the scripture reaches into the container to draw a heavenly treasure glue-on sticker and reads it aloud. Players can take stickers to glue in their journal or tape to the mirror. (5) Player spins the bottle for the next person.

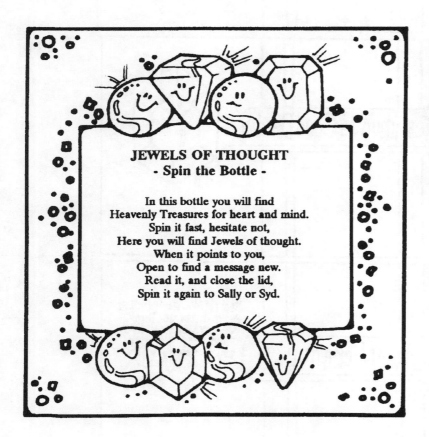

JEWELS OF THOUGHT
- Spin the Bottle -

In this bottle you will find
Heavenly Treasures for heart and mind.
Spin it fast, hesitate not,
Here you will find Jewels of thought.
When it points to you,
Open to find a message new.
Read it, and close the lid,
Spin it again to Sally or Syd.

HEAVEN · SENT · HEAVEN · BOUND

TESTIMONY: "Except ye become converted, and become as little children, ye shall not enter into the kingdom of heaven." (Matthew 18:3)

STRAIT GATE: "Strive to enter in at the strait gate: for many, I say unto you, will seek to enter in, and shall not be able." (Luke 13:24)

CHOOSE THE RIGHT: "If ye know these things, happy are ye if ye do them." (John 13:17)

KEEP TRYING: "Behold, we count them happy which endure." (James 5:11)

 STUDY SCRIPTURES: "They received the word with readiness of mind, and searched the scriptures daily." (Acts 17:11) "Study ... the word of truth." (2 Timothy 2:15)

 KEEP COMMANDMENTS: "For this is the love of God, that we keep his commandments." (1 John 5:3)

GET WISDOM: "The holy scriptures ... are able to make thee wise unto salvation through faith which is in Christ Jesus. All scripture is given by inspiration of God, ... for instruction in righteousness: That the man of God be perfect." (2 Timothy 3:15-17)

LOVE: "If a man say, I love God, and hateth his brother, he is a liar: for he that loveth not his brother whom he hath seen, how can he love God whom he hath not seen?" (1 John 4:20)

 SCRIPTURES TELL OF JESUS: "Search the scriptures; for in them ye think ye have eternal life; and they are they which testify of me." (John 5:39)

LOVE: "A new commandment I give unto you, That ye love one another; as I have loved you, that ye also love one another." (John 13:34)

 PRAYER: "Your Father [in Heaven] knoweth what things ye have need of, before ye ask him." (Matthew 6:8)

BELIEVE IN JESUS: "I am come a light into the world, that whosoever believeth on me should not abide in darkness." (John 12:46)

TESTIMONY: "Wherefore I give you to understand, that no man ... can say that Jesus is the Lord, but by the Holy Ghost." (1 Corinthians 12:3)

CHOOSE THE RIGHT: "Be ye therefore perfect, even as your Father which is in heaven is perfect." (Matthew 5:48)

 PRAYER: "When thou prayest, enter into thy closet, and when thou hast shut thy door, pray to thy Father which is in secret; and thy Father which seeth in secret shall reward thee openly." (Matthew 6:6)

LET YOUR LIGHT SHINE: "Ye are the light of the world ... Let your light so shine before men, that they may see your good works, and glorify your Father which is in heaven." (Matthew 5:14-16)

SEEK HEAVEN: "Seek ye first the kingdom of God, and his righteousness; and all these things shall be added unto you." (Matthew 6:33)

BELIEVE & BE BAPTIZED: "He that believeth and is baptized shall be saved; but he that believeth not shall be damned." (Mark 16:16)

HEAVEN: "Not every one that saith unto me, Lord, Lord, shall enter into the kingdom of heaven; but he that doeth the will of my Father which is in heaven." (Matthew 7:21)

JESUS IS HEAVEN SENT: "And no man hath ascended up to heaven, but he that came down from heaven, even the Son of man which is in heaven." (John 3:13)

HEAVEN: "He that endureth to the end shall be saved." (Matthew 10:22)

SCRIPTURE WARNING: "Jesus answered and said unto them, Ye do err, not knowing the scriptures, nor the power of God." (Matthew 22:29)

TREASURES ON EARTH AND HEAVEN: "Jesus ... saith unto them, Children, how hard is it for them that trust in riches to enter into the kingdom of God! It is easier for a camel to go through the eye of a needle, than for a rich man to enter into the kingdom of God." (Mark 10:24-25)

TWO GREAT COMMANDMENTS: "Jesus said unto him, Thou shalt love the Lord thy God with all thy heart, and with all thy soul, and with all thy mind. This is the first and great commandment. And the second is like unto it, Thou shalt love thy neighbour as thyself." (Matthew 22:37-39)

BELIEVE IN JESUS: "He that believeth on the Son hath everlasting life: and he that believeth not the Son shall not see life; but the wrath of God abideth on him." (John 3:36)

HEAVEN BOUND: "Verily I say unto you, Whatsoever ye shall bind on earth shall be bound in heaven: and whatsoever ye shall loose on earth shall be loosed in heaven." (Matthew 18:18)

CHILDREN: "Jesus ... said unto them, Suffer the little children to come unto me, and forbid them not: for of such is the kingdom of God." (Mark 10:14)

ETERNAL LIFE: "And this is life eternal, that they might know thee the only true God, and Jesus Christ, whom thou hast sent." (John 17:3)

FAITH: "If I have told you earthly things, and ye believe not, how shall ye believe, if I tell you heavenly things?" (John 3:12)

STRENGTH: "Put on the whole armour of God, that ye may be able to stand against the wiles of the devil." (Ephesians 6:11)

FAITH & WORKS: "Faith, if it hath not works, is dead." (James 2:17)

COMMANDMENTS: "If ye love me, keep my commandments." (John 14:15)

TRUTH: "Know the truth, and the truth shall make you free." (John 8:32)

DOING GOOD: "If ye know these things, happy are ye if ye do them." (John 13:17)

EARTHLY
Treasures
LOSE A TURN

HEAVENLY
Treasures
READ SCRIPTURE
FROM BOTTLE

EARTHLY
Treasures
LOSE A TURN

HEAVENLY
Treasures
READ SCRIPTURE
FROM BOTTLE

EARTHLY
Treasures
LOSE A TURN

HEAVENLY
Treasures
READ SCRIPTURE
FROM BOTTLE

EARTHLY
Treasures
LOSE A TURN

HEAVENLY
Treasures
READ SCRIPTURE
FROM BOTTLE

EARTHLY
Treasures
LOSE A TURN

HEAVENLY
Treasures
READ SCRIPTURE
FROM BOTTLE

EARTHLY
Treasures
LOSE A TURN

HEAVENLY
Treasures
READ SCRIPTURE
FROM BOTTLE

EARTHLY
Treasures
LOSE A TURN

HEAVENLY
Treasures
READ SCRIPTURE
FROM BOTTLE

EARTHLY
Treasures
LOSE A TURN

HEAVENLY
Treasures
READ SCRIPTURE
FROM BOTTLE

SEEDS OF FAITH: My Testimony Is Growing

SONG: "Search, Ponder, and Pray," page 78 in the *Children's Songbook**.

INTRODUCTION:

Our testimony is like a watermelon. It starts to grow from a tiny seed of faith. It grows as we read the scriptures, pray, and live the commandments as Jesus did.

The New Testament tells of his life. Think of each book as a seed of faith. Matthew, Mark, Luke, John, and others walked and talked with Jesus. They wrote of his life. Your faith can increase as you read about our Savior, Jesus Christ.

SEEDS OF FAITH:
My Testimony Is Growing
FILE FOLDER
SHOW-AND-TELL:

CREATE: Cut out cue cards (pages 12-13) and file folder label (page iii). Color and cut out visuals (pages 14-15). Glue the label on file folder.

PRESENT: Read cue cards and place visuals on folder with tape or Velcro.
OPTION: Attach strings.

ACTIVITY: Seeds of Faith Watermelon Bust! Beanbag Toss. Objective: To learn the books of the New Testament. See details on page 16.

THOUGHT TREAT: Seeds of Faith Watermelon Cookies. See details on page 111.

Children's Songbook is published by The Church of Jesus Christ of Latter-day Saints, Salt Lake City, Utah.

FILE FOLDER SHOW-AND-TELL:

#1 **SEEDS OF FAITH: My Testimony Is Growing**
<u>Our testimony is like this watermelon.</u>
It starts to grow from a tiny seed of faith.

It grows as we:
- ♥ Read the scriptures,
- ♥ Pray to Heavenly Father,
- ♥ Keep his commandments, and
- ♥ Share our testimony with others.

We can gain a testimony of Jesus as you read the New Testament and other scriptures. Think of each New Testament book as a seed of faith. The more you learn about Jesus and his testimony, the more your testimony will grow.

The New Testament books are Matthew, Mark, Luke, John, The Acts, Romans, 1st and 2nd Corinthians, Galatians, Ephesians, Philippians, Colossians, 1st and 2nd Thessalonians, 1st and 2nd Timothy, Titus, Philemon, Hebrews, James, 1st and 2nd Peter, 1st, 2nd, and 3rd John, Jude, and Revelation.

#2 Who wrote the Bible?

The <u>Old Testament is the first half of the Bible</u>. This tells of the people who lived before Jesus. Prophets like Adam, Moses, and Abraham had visions and dreams about Jesus. They told the people that Jesus was coming to save the world from sin.

The <u>New Testament is the second half of the Bible</u>. The apostles and others who knew Jesus wrote of his life. They wrote the New Testament books. Jesus chose 12 disciples to help him lead his church. They walked and talked with Jesus and told of his life.

Jesus told his apostles how to plant seeds of faith, and they could work miracles. They could hold the priesthood and heal the sick as he did. They saw many miracles, and they loved Jesus.

#3 The New Testament tells us about the life of Jesus here on the earth:

♥ <u>Jesus came as a baby, born of Mary</u> in Bethlehem. Jesus was raised by Mary and by Joseph, who was a carpenter. They taught him the scriptures from the Old Testament and how to choose the right.

♥ <u>Jesus is the Son of God</u>, who is our Heavenly Father.

♥ <u>Jesus taught the people to have faith</u>. He taught them how to be happy. He taught in parables, which are stories that tell us how to get to heaven.

♥ <u>Jesus healed the sick and performed many miracles</u>. HE PLANTED SEEDS OF FAITH ALONG THE WAY. WE CAN FOLLOW HIM AND GROW IN FAITH.

♥ <u>Jesus suffered for our sins, died, and was resurrected</u> so that we might be resurrected and live again.

FILE FOLDER SHOW-AND-TELL:

#4   **What do the years B.C. and A.D. mean?**

The years B.C. are the years BEFORE CHRIST was born. The years A.D. were the years AFTER DEATH (after Jesus died).

The Old Testament was written in the years B.C., before Jesus came. Many people worshiped gods of stone. The prophet Moses told the people to worship Heavenly Father, and not idols. Moses received the Ten Commandments from Heavenly Father, and told the people, "These are laws to obey now, and Jesus will come to tell us more."

Jesus came after hundreds of years. He lived a perfect life and taught us how to get to heaven. He told his disciples, *"Yet a little while am I with you, and then I go unto him that sent me"* (John 7:33). He was going to Heavenly Father. But he didn't leave us alone. He sent the Holy Ghost as a comforter and guide. Jesus wants us to have faith that he will come again.

#5   **Where did Jesus and the apostles live?**

☐   Jerusalem, Galilee, and other nearby desert places.

☐   Here Jesus taught about faith. Faith is hope for things you can't see, but which are true. Jesus said this about faith:

♥ *"Have faith in God."* (Mark 11:22)

♥ *"Therefore I say unto you, What things soever ye desire, when ye pray, believe that ye receive them, and ye shall have them."* (Mark 11:24)

♥ *"I have prayed for thee, that thy faith fail not: and when thou art converted, strengthen thy brethren."* (Luke 22:32)

Jesus preached faith and repentance. He wanted us to have faith in our Heavenly Father, pray and believe, and then share our testimony with others.

#6   **We Can Plant Seeds of Faith Every Day**

We can increase our faith in Heavenly Father and Jesus.
We can plant seeds of faith every day.

1. **READ** the New Testament and other scriptures.
2. **LIVE** as Jesus lived, walk in his steps. Ask ourselves before you do something: What would Jesus do?
3. **TELL** others the stories of Jesus:

♥ He taught the people about faith, repentance, and baptism.

♥ He healed the sick, fed 5,000 people with only 5 loaves of bread and two fish, calmed the seas, and walked on water to teach the apostles to have faith.

♥ He taught with parables to guide us back to our heavenly home.

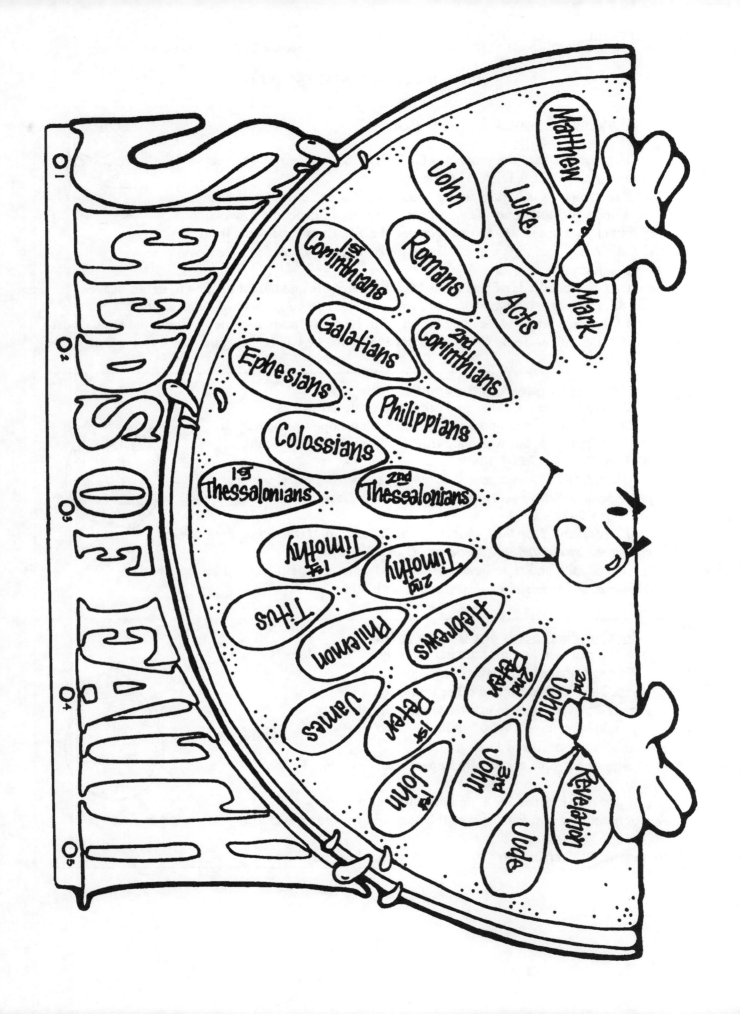

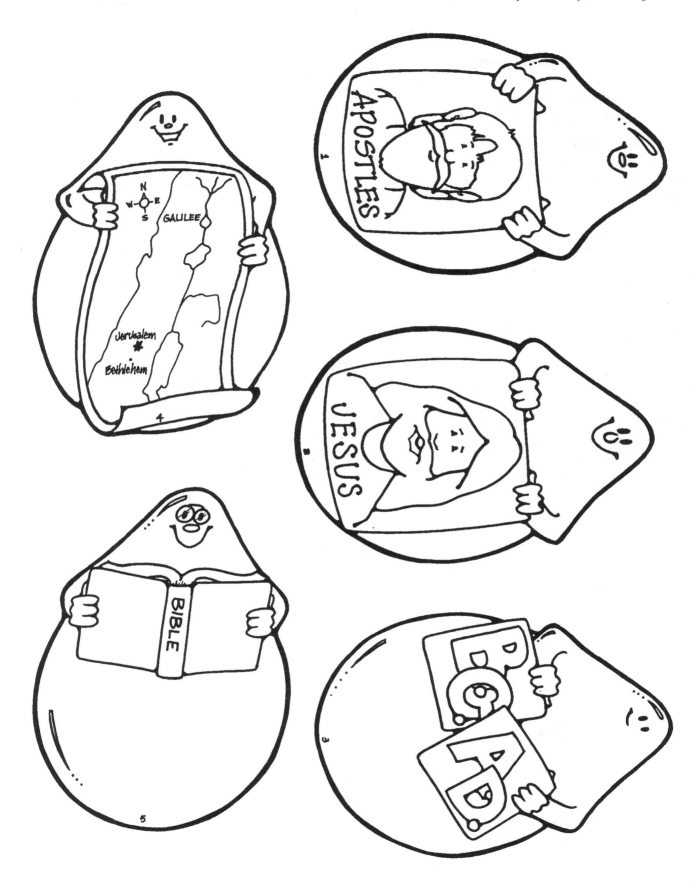

ACTIVITY: Seeds of Faith Watermelon Bust! Beanbag Toss

OBJECTIVE: To learn the books of the New Testament.
As players toss beanbag into a giant watermelon seed, they name the books that are written on their beanbag.

TO MAKE GAME:
1. Color and cut out Watermelon Bust! images (shown right on pages 17-20) and mount on watermelon on poster paper.
2. Cut a hole where indicated (through poster paper).
3. To make beanbags, color and cut out beans (page 19). Fill a plastic sandwich bag with beans, rice, or popcorn. Seal bag and place another bag on top, placing bean images inside.
4. To make prizes, color and cut out bookmarks and glasses for each child. Tape side frames to glasses and cut out centers.

TO PLAY:
1. Set up game by taping Watermelon Bust! poster to a snack bar or chair so beanbags can be thrown through giant seed hole.

*Pronunciations of the Books of the New Testament:
  Matthew (math ū)   **Mark** (märk)   **Luke** (lūk)
    John (jŏn)   **Acts** (ăkts)   **Romans** (rō-manz)
  Corinthians (ka-rin' thē-anz)   **Galatians** (ga-lāsh' anz)
    Ephesians (i-fē: zhanz)   **Philippians** (fi-lip' ē onz)
        Colossians (ka-lŏsh' anz)
  Thessalonians (thĕs a: lō nēanz)   **Timothy** (tĭm' a-thē)
      Titus (tītas)   **Philemon** (fi-lē' mən)
  Hebrews (hē' brōōz)   **James** (jāmz)   **Peter** (pē'tar)
    John (jŏn)   **Jude** (jūd)   **Revelation** (rĕv'ə-lā' shən)

2. Practice pronouncing the New Testament books (shown on the beanbag seeds). Pronunciations are shown above. Play game (rules below).
3. Reward winners with a New Testament bookmark or "Faith is Cool!" sunglasses (shown below).

RULES FOR SMALL GROUP (5-8 players):
1. First player takes a New Testament beanbag and stands four to five feed from game board. Player names one of the books of the New Testament written on his beanbag, and tries to toss it into the giant seed pocket.

2. If beanbag makes it into the giant seed pocket, player receives ten (10) points.
3. The first player to receive 100 points wins.

LARGE GROUP:
Play without keeping score, clapping as each player scores. See #1 above.

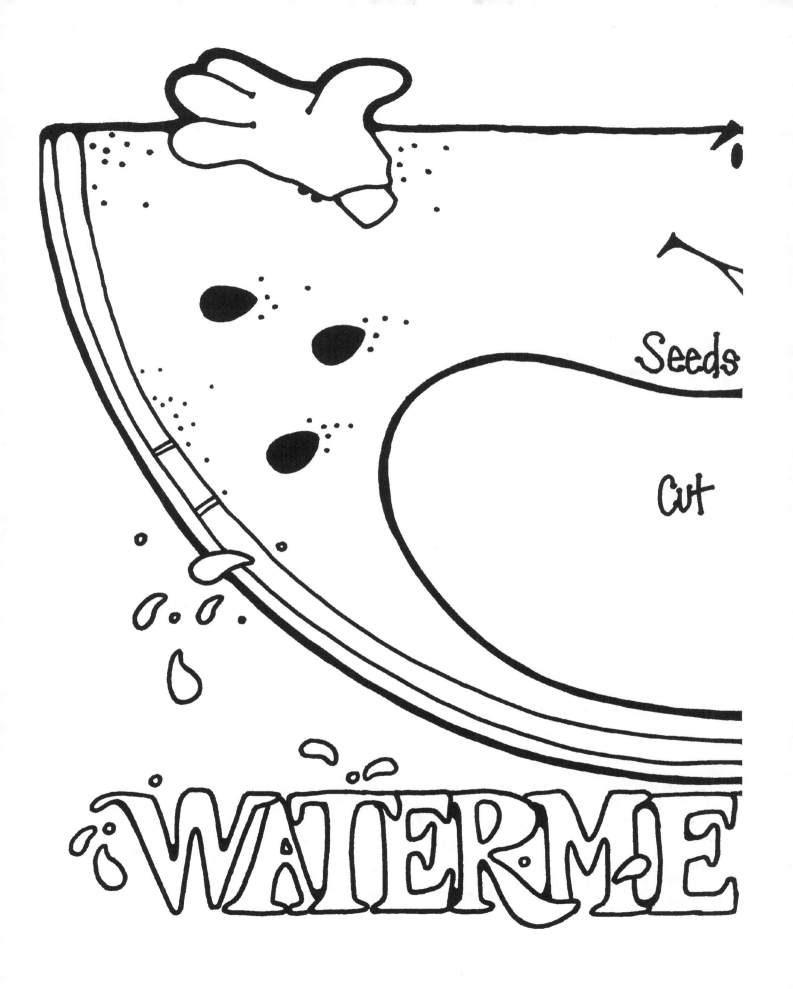

PATTERN: Seeds of Faith: Watermelon Bust game and beanbag labels ♥ Copy on cardstock paper.

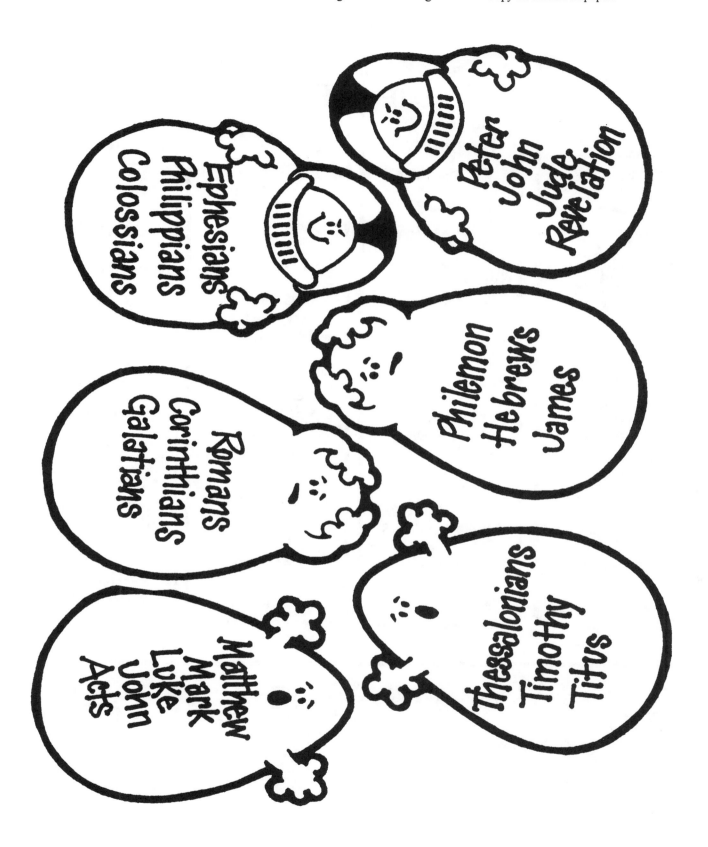

PATTERN: Prize (bookmark)

Faith is hope for things you can't see but are true.

Made in the shade with Heavenly Father's plan!

File Folder FAMILY HOME EVENING

ANGEL TELLS OF TWO BIRTHS: John and Jesus

SONG: "He Sent His Son," page 34 in the *Children's Songbook**.

INTRODUCTION:

The Angel Gabriel appeared to Zacharias, Mary, and Joseph, telling them that John the Baptist and Jesus would be born. John would tell the people that Jesus is coming, and would baptize Jesus. Jesus would come to tell us of Heavenly Father's plan.

Did you know that John and Jesus were cousins? John's mother, Elisabeth, and Jesus' mother, Mary, were also cousins.

Let's go to a family reunion and meet the kinfolk of John and Jesus.

ANGEL TELLS OF TWO BIRTHS: John and Jesus FILE FOLDER SHOW-AND-TELL:

CREATE: Cut out cue cards (pages 23-24) and file folder label (page iii). Color and cut out visuals (pages 25-26). Glue the label on file folder.

PRESENT: Read cue cards and place visuals on folder with tape or Velcro.

ACTIVITY:
Baby News Match spoons game (shown left). See page 27 for details.

THOUGHT TREAT:

<u>Angel Food Cake and Baby Love Milk</u>. Serve angel food cake with milk. Detailed on page 111.

Children's Songbook is published by The Church of Jesus Christ of Latter-day Saints, Salt Lake City, Utah.

FILE FOLDER SHOW-AND-TELL PLAY: One person can do file folder play, moving the characters in and out, or several people can participate showing their characters and saying their parts. Use the file folder as a stage.

#1 **ANGEL TELLS OF TWO BIRTHS: John and Jesus:** The following is like a stage play. Imagine with us as we move the characters back and forth off the stage (file folder) as we tell the story of the Angel Gabriel telling of two births, John and Jesus.

NARRATOR: Elisabeth was married to Zacharias. They lived in Jerusalem. They obeyed God's commandments. They were both very old, but they still prayed for a child.

ELISABETH said, "It would be so wonderful if we could have a baby. I love children. It would be so nice to have a little son or a daughter to love and take care of.

ZACHARIAS: It sure would. But, as you know, we are too old to have children. I have lost hope.

EXIT Elisabeth

#2 **NARRATOR:** Zacharias was a priest and worked in the temple. One day the Angel Gabriel appeared to him.

GABRIEL: Don't be afraid. Heavenly Father has sent me here to bless you and Elisabeth. God has answered your prayers. Elisabeth will have a baby. His name will be John. God has a work for John to do. He will hold the priesthood of God, and tell the people about Jesus Christ, the Son of God. John will be a righteous prophet.

ZACHARIAS: I do not believe you. Elisabeth is too old to have a baby.

GABRIEL: God sent me to tell you that this is true. Because you do not believe what God has said, you will not be able to speak or hear until John is born.

NARRATOR: Zacharias came out of the temple and could not speak. Elisabeth now was going to have a baby. Baby John was the child they had always dreamed of.

EXIT Zacharias and Angel

NARRATOR: The Angel Gabriel came to Mary.

GABRIEL: Be not afraid. God loves you and wants to bless you more than any other woman, as you will have a special baby boy. His name will be Jesus. He will be the king of all righteous people.

MARY: But I do not have a husband.

GABRIEL: With God, nothing shall be impossible. Jesus will be the Son of God.

EXIT Mary and Gabriel

MARY: I will obey and be the mother of Jesus.

FILE FOLDER SHOW-AND-TELL:

#4

NARRATOR: Mary and Joseph lived in Nazareth. They were righteous. They always tried to choose the right. Mary and Joseph loved each other and wanted to be married.

NARRATOR: The angel appeared to Joseph in a dream.

ANGEL: Mary's baby is the Son of God. Take Mary as your wife and name the baby Jesus. Jesus will be the Savior of the world.

JOSEPH: I will obey.

EXIT Mary

EXIT Angel and Joseph

#5

NARRATOR: Mary visited her cousin Elisabeth. The two women were to have special children: Jesus Christ and John the Baptist. They were blessed more than any other women. Because Elisabeth and Mary were cousins, the babies John and Jesus would also be cousins.

EXIT Mary, Elisabeth, Baby John, and Jesus

#6

NARRATOR: Elisabeth and Zacharias' baby son was born. Friends gathered around. Everyone was so happy! Friends thought Elisabeth should name the baby Zacharias, after the father. Elisabeth said, "No." They asked Zacharias what to name the baby. He could not speak, so he wrote the name JOHN. Then Zacharias was able to speak and hear. He was filled with the Holy Ghost and thanked God for baby John. Zacharias told the people that Jesus would be born soon.

#7

NARRATOR: Joseph and Mary had to go to Bethlehem to pay their taxes. Mary was very tired, as she would have the baby soon. Many people were in Bethlehem, and there were no rooms left.

JOSEPH: I found a place where you can have the baby. It is a stable, a place for animals, but the baby will be warm.

MARY: Thank you, Joseph. I am so tired.

NARRATOR: Mary had the baby Jesus, and a star shone brightly over the manger to direct the shepherds and wise men to the humble stable. They came, and saw the baby Jesus wrapped in swaddling clothes, lying in a manger. Mary and Joseph were so happy that they could help take care of Jesus, the Savior of us all.

THE END

PATTERN: Show-and-Tell presentation and Baby News Match game

PATTERN: Show-and-Tell presentation and Baby News Match game

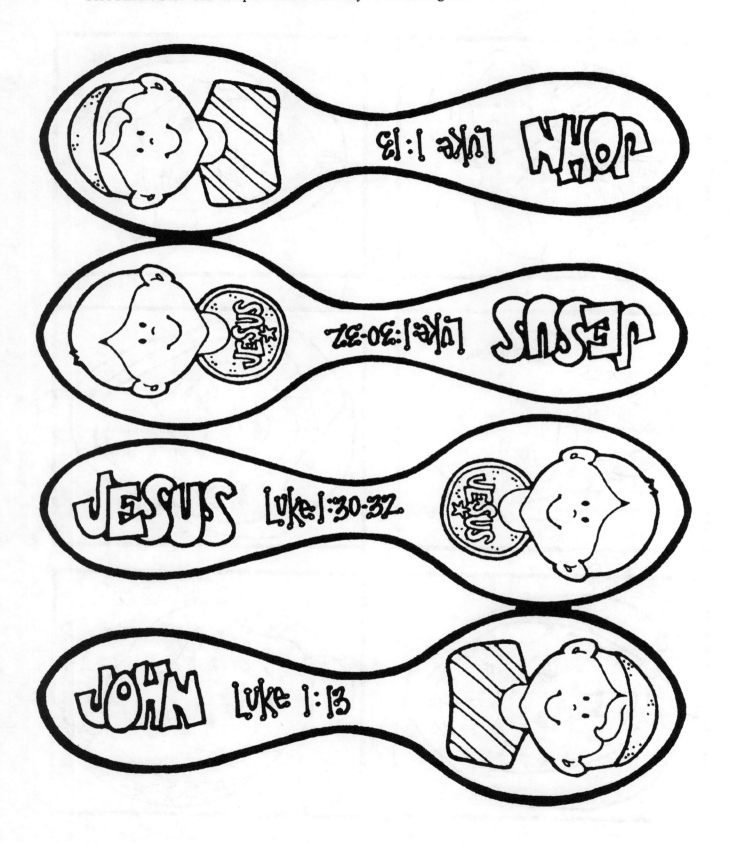

ACTIVITY: Baby News Match Spoons Game

OBJECTIVE: Match character cards to get acquainted with Elisabeth, Zacharias, Baby John, Mary, Joseph, and Baby Jesus. Make a match and grab for spoons!

TO MAKE GAME: (1) Copy and cut out four sets of cards (page 25) and 8 sets of baby spoons (page 26). Glue baby spoons back to back.

TO SET UP GAME: (1) Place the John and Jesus baby spoons in the center of table or floor.
(2) Place cards face down in a circle with John and Jesus baby spoons in the center.

TO PLAY: (1) Players take turns turning two cards over to try to make a match. (2) As soon as player makes a match, player says "BABY NEWS!" before other players say "YOU SNOOZE." Player grabs a spoon in the center as he says "BABY NEWS!"

POINTS EARNED: Spoons are worth 20 points. Matched cards are worth 10 points.

RULES: YOU DON'T WANT TO BE CAUGHT SNOOZING (sleeping):
1. If player snoozes, then the player who says "YOU SNOOZE" can grab a spoon (worth 20 points).
2. Returned Matched Cards Rule: If the player is caught snoozing (not saying "BABY NEWS" before the other player says "YOU SNOOZE"), then that player has to return his or her matched cards to the center. Place returned match cards in a stack (don't put back into the pile). After all cards are matched, these returned cards can be placed in a pile so players can match them.
4. Keep playing until the first player earns 100 or the designated time is up. Remember, if you snooze, you lose!

PRIZE: Copy Baby Love Milk images below and create refrigerator magnets or glue-on stickers.

File Folder FAMILY HOME EVENING
LET'S CELEBRATE the Birth of Jesus

SONG: "When Joseph Went to Bethlehem," page 38 in the *Children's Songbook**.

INTRODUCTION:

Tell family, "Let's celebrate the birth of Jesus. Let's imagine what it was like when Mary, the mother of Jesus, learned she would have a baby, the son of Heavenly Father. Let's travel with them to Bethlehem, where there was no room in the inn. Let's learn of shepherds and wise men who traveled far to find the Christ child. They followed a star that shown bright that special night. Then, as soon as Jesus was born, he was in danger. Let's learn what happened."

LET'S CELEBRATE the Birth of Jesus
FILE FOLDER SHOW-AND-TELL:
CREATE: Cut out cue cards (pages 29-30) and file folder label (page iii). Color and cut out visuals (pages 31-32). Glue the label on file folder.
PRESENT: Read cue cards and place visuals on folder with tape or Velcro.

ACTIVITY:

Star Bright That Special Night Musical Chairs. Color and cut out stars (page 33).
TO SET UP GAME: Tape large star to a chair and place chair in the center of the room.
TELL FAMILY: "Jesus is the son of Heavenly Father. The night the baby Jesus was born in Bethlehem, an angel told the shepherds and wise men how to find him. The people of the New Testament times had waited for Jesus for hundreds of years. At last he was coming. The angel told them to follow a special star that was shining brightly that special night" [point to star on chair].

TO PLAY: Leader plays or sings Christmas songs or music as players march in a circle around the star chair. When music stops, the first person to sit on chair gets to hold the small star and say, "Jesus is the star we've waited for." Then tell how you would feel, or what you would do or say if you were to visit the baby Jesus. Then that person leaves the circle. **ORNAMENT OPTION:** Have a testimony meeting, telling how you feel about the Savior. Write key words from your testimonies on the back of the stars. Paper punch stars, attach a string, and tie onto the Christmas tree. Laminate for durability. Then each year take out the ornaments to remember this special family home evening, as you do this FILE FOLDER SHOW-AND-TELL presentation.
THOUGHT TREAT: Star Bright Cookies. Cut out sugar cookie dough into star shapes. Sprinkle bright yellow sugar on top and bake. To make colored sugar, place sugar in a zip-close bag, add a few drops of yellow food coloring, close bag, and mix together.
ACTIVITY: As you eat each star corner, name five ways you will follow Jesus.

**Children's Songbook* is published by The Church of Jesus Christ of Latter-day Saints, Salt Lake City, Utah.

FILE FOLDER SHOW-AND-TELL:

#1   ## LET'S CELEBRATE the Birth of Jesus

Let's celebrate the birth of Jesus by making a cake. Let's put the candles on his birthday cake as we learn six things that came to pass.

The Angel Gabriel appeared to Mary and asked her if she would be the mother of Jesus. At first she was afraid. But after she learned that Jesus would be the Son of God, she said yes.

Then the Angel appeared to Joseph and asked him to take care of Mary and the baby Jesus. Joseph said yes. They knew Jesus was a special child, the son of Heavenly Father.

#2

The Roman king made a law that everyone had to pay taxes to their kingdom. So, *"All went to be taxed, everyone into his own city"* (Luke 2:3).

Joseph took Mary and went to the city of David, which is called Bethlehem. Mary and Joseph lived in Galilee. They went out of the city of Nazareth into Judaea, to the city of David.

They had to travel far. Sixty-five miles is a long way to ride a donkey or to walk. It was very hard for Mary to travel, as the baby Jesus would soon be born.

#3

After a long journey, Mary and Joseph came to Bethlehem. There were many people there paying taxes, and all the rooms were filled. There was no room in the inn for Joseph and Mary. Mary was heavy with child, and they needed a place to stay.

The only place they could find was a stable, a place where animals live. Jesus was born in this stable. Mary carefully wrapped him in swaddling clothes and laid him in a manger. Swaddling clothes were a soft linen cloth. A manger is a trough or open box where horses and cattle feed.

THIS WAS A SPECIAL DAY.

FILE FOLDER SHOW-AND-TELL:

#4

An angel of God came to shepherds in the fields near Bethlehem that special night. The shepherds were afraid. The angel told them not to fear, that he came with great news: The Savior, Jesus Christ, was born that night in Bethlehem, and they would find him in a manger.

They rushed to Bethlehem, where they saw the baby Jesus in a manger. Mary and Joseph were with the baby.

When the shepherds left the stable, they were so happy that they had seen the Savior. They told many people what they had seen.

#5

Wise men from another land came looking for the baby Jesus. The prophets said he would become their king.

In Jerusalem, King Herod was worried that he would no longer be the king. He told the wise men to go to Bethlehem and find the child so he could worship him too.

The wise men followed that special star to Bethlehem. The star shone over the stable where Jesus was born. The wise men were happy to see the Christ child. They knelt down and worshipped Jesus, and gave him gifts.

They were warned by an angel not to tell King Herod where the baby was. They went home.

#6

King Herod was jealous. He worried that Jesus would be the king of Jerusalem.

He wanted to kill Jesus. He knew Jesus was a baby, so he commanded his soldiers to kill all the babies in Bethlehem and the places nearby. This way Jesus would be killed.

Joseph was warned to save Jesus. An angel visited Joseph and told him to take Mary and the baby Jesus to Egypt. They would be far away from Herod's soldiers. Joseph obeyed, and Jesus' life was spared.

After Herod died, the angel visited Joseph and told him it was safe to go home. They went to Nazareth.

File Folder FAMILY HOME EVENING

CREATING ME: I'm Trying to Be Like Jesus

OPENING SONG: "I'm Trying to Be Like Jesus," page 78 in the *Children's Songbook**.

INTRODUCTION:

Show a picture of Jesus and say: "Heavenly Father sent his Son Jesus Christ to the earth to show us how to live. If we try to be like Jesus, we can find eternal happiness. He came to show us the way back to our heavenly home. Each day we can learn to be like Jesus: *'Jesus increased in wisdom, and stature, and in favour with God and man'* (Luke 2:52)."

CREATING ME:
I'm Trying to Be Like Jesus
FILE FOLDER
SHOW-AND-TELL:

CREATE: Cut out cue cards (pages 35-36) and file folder label (page iii). Color and cut out visuals (pages 37-39). Glue the label on file folder.

PRESENT: Read cue cards and place visuals on folder with tape or Velcro.

ACTIVITY:

Pop Into the Future! Balloon Bustin' Good Time. See page 40 for details.

OBJECTIVE:
To learn fun goals to balance life as Jesus did (read Luke 2:52): Mental, Physical, Spiritual, and Social.

Pop Into the Future!

I'll pray morning and night to keep heaven in sight!

THOUGHT TREAT:
<u>Goal Graham Cracker Sandwiches</u>. See details on page 112.

*Children's Songbook is published by The Church of Jesus Christ of Latter-day Saints, Salt Lake City, Utah.

FILE FOLDER SHOW-AND-TELL:

#1   <u>CREATING ME: I'm Trying to Be Like Jesus</u>

Jesus As a Boy:

♥ In Luke 2:52 we learn that *"Jesus increased in wisdom, and stature, and in favour with God and man."*

♥ Jesus wants us to be like him, as he knows the way back to heaven. Jesus told us about Heavenly Father's plan. He told us what we need to do to be happy.

♥ Let's learn about Jesus and how he balanced his life. "Balance" means he knew what to say and do at all times. He used his mind. He had a strong body. He had a good spirit and loved others. Jesus was perfect. He is the Son of God.

#2   **Jesus Increased in Wisdom:**

♥ Jesus increased in wisdom. Wisdom means to use your mind. Jesus went to school and listened to his teachers. He learned how to be a carpenter from Joseph. He learned love and obedience from his mother, Mary.

♥ He prayed and Heavenly Father taught him what he needed to know.

♥ When Jesus was 12, Mary and Joseph took him to Jerusalem. When Jesus was missing, they found him in the temple. He was talking to several wise men. They answered many of his questions. Then he answered their questions. They were amazed at how much Jesus knew.
Mary and Joseph were also surprised at how much Jesus knew.

♥ Let's study, listen, and pray to increase in wisdom, as Jesus did.

#3   **Jesus Increased in Stature:**

♥ In Luke 2:40, the Apostle Luke tells of Jesus: *"And the child grew, and waxed strong in spirit, filled with wisdom; and the grace of God was upon him."*

♥ Jesus increased in stature. He grew strong.

♥ Jesus ate good food to keep his body strong. He walked many miles as he didn't have a car to drive or a bicycle to ride. Sometimes Jesus rode a donkey.

♥ Jesus was a carpenter and helped Joseph. He had to lift heavy wood, and he used his hands to work very hard.

♥ We can be like Jesus as we make our bodies strong.

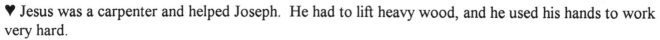

FILE FOLDER SHOW-AND-TELL:

#4 **Jesus Increased in Favour with God:**

♥ Jesus read from the scriptures and prayed to Heavenly Father often.

♥ Jesus had to prepare himself for his mission, to teach the people about Heavenly Father's plan. When Jesus was in the wilderness, the devil came and asked him to eat, saying: *"If thou be the Son of God, command that these stones be made bread. But he answered and said, It is written, Man shall not live by bread alone, but by every word that proceedeth out of the mouth of God"* (Matthew 4:4).

♥ Jesus was able to say, "NO," to temptation, because he knew he had to fast to learn more about Heavenly Father's plan. We too can say, "NO" to temptation and "YES" to choosing the right.

#5 **Jesus Increased in Favour with Man:**

♥ This SOCIAL balloon reminds us that Jesus loved others. He loved his friends, family, and neighbors. Jesus said to love your neighbor as you would love yourself (Luke 10:27).

♥ Jesus called 12 men to be his apostles. He asked them to help lead his church. They were like missionary companions. They went with him to teach others.

♥ Jesus said we should love everyone. To show his love, he taught thousands of people about Heavenly Father's plan. He healed the sick and the crippled, and even raised a girl and a man from the dead.

♥ He loved little children. He told his disciples to bring the little children to him, then he blessed them. Let's follow Jesus and love others.

#6 **I'm Trying to Be Like Jesus:**

♥ Let's be creative. Let's say: "CREATE ME!"

♥ A lawyer asked Jesus how we can have eternal life. This means we would live with Heavenly Father again. Jesus said to the lawyer, *"Thou shalt love the Lord thy God with all thy heart, and with all thy soul, and with all thy strength, and with all thy mind; and thy neighbour as thyself"* (Luke 10:25-27).

♥ CREATE ME! means to balance your life. Let's think about what we need to do to gain eternal life. We want to live with Heavenly Father again someday, so let's make every day count. Let's live as Jesus did.

FILE FOLDER PRESENTATION

FILE FOLDER PRESENTATION

FILE FOLDER PRESENTATION

ACTIVITY: Pop Into the Future!
Balloon Bustin' Good Time
OBJECTIVE: To learn fun goals to help balance your life as Jesus did.
YOU'LL NEED a balloon for each player.
TO MAKE: (1) Cut out and roll up wordstrips (below and page 43). (2) Stuff a wordstrip inside each balloon (or 2-3 wordstrips per balloon). (3) Blow up each balloon and tie. (4) Take turns sitting on a balloon and reading the wordstrip (or 2-3 wordstrips) aloud (not letting the others see the wordstrip). Family tries to guess the balanced life area, i.e., Mental, Physical, Spiritual, Social.

OPTION: Lay wordstrips face down on the table instead of stuffing them into balloons.

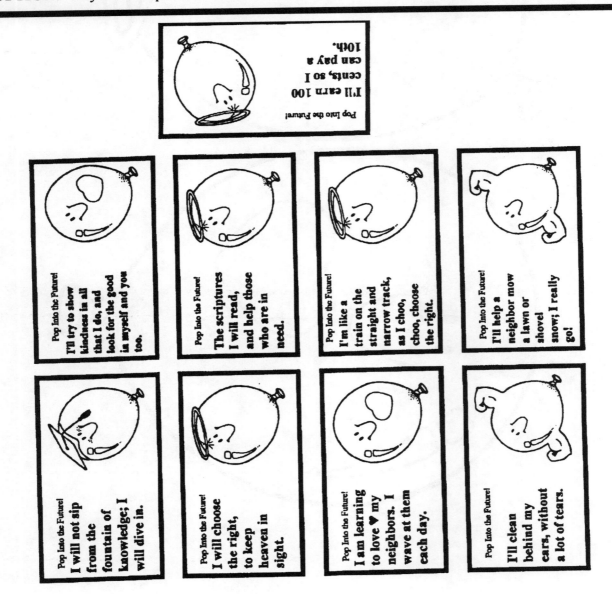

Pop Into the Future!
I'll earn 100 cents, so I can pay a 10th.

Pop Into the Future!
I'll try to show kindness in all that I do, and look for the good in myself and you too.

Pop Into the Future!
The scriptures I will read, and help those who are in need.

Pop Into the Future!
I'm like a train on the straight and narrow track, as I choo, choo, choo, choose the right.

Pop Into the Future!
I'll help a neighbor mow a lawn or shovel snow; I really go!

Pop Into the Future!
I will not sip from the fountain of knowledge; I will dive in.

Pop Into the Future!
I will choose the right, to keep heaven in sight.

Pop Into the Future!
I am learning to love ♥ my neighbors. I wave at them each day.

Pop Into the Future!
I'll clean behind my ears, without a lot of tears.

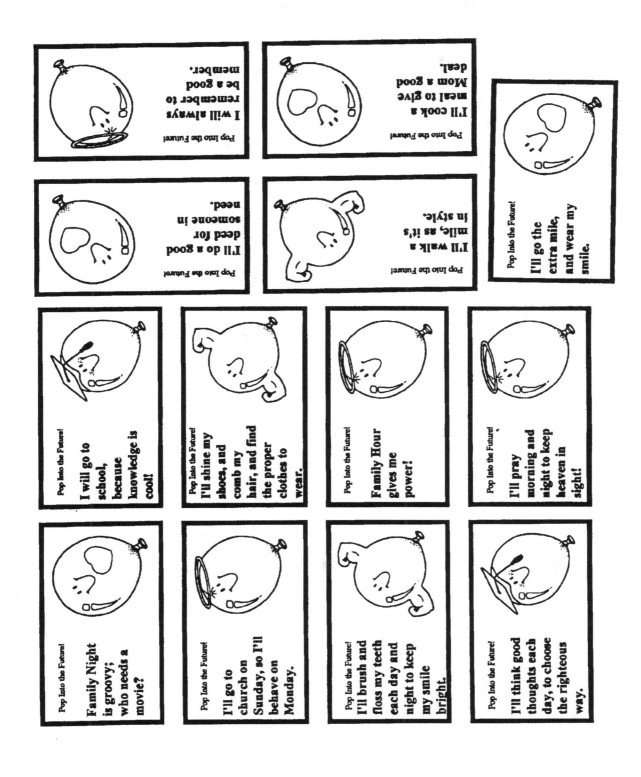

File Folder FAMILY HOME EVENING
FISHERS OF MEN: Jesus Chose 12 Apostles

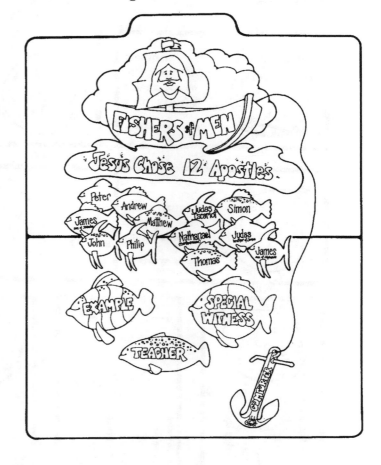

SONG: "I Feel My Savior's Love," page 74 in the *Children's Songbook**.

INTRODUCTION: Jesus chose 12 apostles to be fishers of men. They *"straightway left their nets, and followed him"* (Matthew 4:17-20). We too can be fishers of men. We can be an example to others, share the gospel with them, and bear our testimony. Let's learn how to be a disciple of Jesus Christ. Let's remember the Comforter he left. The Holy Ghost can be an anchor in our lives. If we listen and obey the still small voice, the Holy Ghost will guide us out of dangerous waters. It will be our constant companion until Jesus returns.

FISHERS OF MEN:
Jesus Chose 12 Apostles
File Folder Show-and-Tell:

CREATE: Cut out cue cards (pages 43-44) and file folder label (page iii). Color and cut out visuals (pages 45-46). Glue the label on file folder.

PRESENT: Read cue cards and place visuals on folder with tape or Velcro.

ACTIVITY: <u>GO FISH: Disciple Decisions</u>. **OBJECTIVE:** With fish tickets, go fishing for prizes that teach ways to be a missionary or disciple of Jesus.

TO MAKE: Copy fish tickets, a goodie sack and fish-ionary tie (pages 47-48) for each family member to fish for.

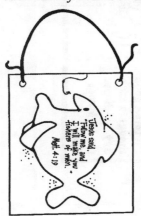

TO SET UP: (1) To make the fish pond curtain, pin the Fishers of Men Jesus Chose 12 Apostles sign (page 45) on a blanket attached to two chairs (with safety pins). (2) Cut out fish tickets (page 48) and give to family members to fish. (3) Attach a string to a pole and to a paper clip.

GO FISH: (1) Attach ticket to paper clip and have family member throw pole over blanket. (2) Someone on the other side gives out prizes: a fish-ionary tie (page 48) tied to a string to place around a child's neck, and a Fishers of Men goodie sack (page 50) filled with fish crackers or gummyfish candy.

FISH-IONARY TIE: Wear tie as you share treats and talk about ways you can be a disciple of Jesus Christ.

THOUGHT TREAT: <u>Jiggly Jelly Fish Pond</u>.
See details on page 112.

**Children's Songbook* is published by The Church of Jesus Christ of Latter-day Saints, Salt Lake City, Utah.

#1

FISHERS OF MEN:
Jesus Chose 12 Apostles.

Jesus and his apostles were FISHERS OF MEN.

Jesus prepared for his mission and then he chose 12 apostles. They were chosen to help Jesus heal the sick and teach men to repent and be baptized, so they could live with Heavenly Father again. First, Jesus prepared for his mission:

♥ Jesus was baptized in the River Jordan, and Heavenly Father said, "*This is my beloved Son, in whom I am well pleased*" (Matthew 3:17).

♥ Jesus fasted and prayed forty days and nights in the wilderness. Satan tempted Jesus, but Jesus said, "No." He was there to learn from Heavenly Father.

♥ Jesus began his mission, saying to the people: "*Repent: for the kingdom of heaven is at hand*" (Matthew 4:17).

#2

While walking by the sea of Galilee, Jesus saw two brethren, Simon called Peter, and Andrew his brother, casting a net into the sea, for they were fishermen. "*And he saith unto them, Follow me, and I will make you fishers of men. And they straightway left their nets, and followed him*" (Matthew 4:19-20).

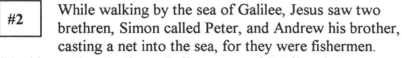

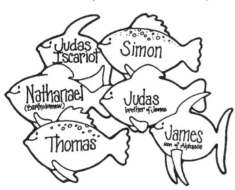

The 12 apostles Jesus chose were to be fishers of men, to convert the people to the gospel of Jesus Christ. He ordained them to the priesthood.

They were Peter, James (son of Zebedee), John, Andrew, Matthew, Philip, Judas (the brother of James), Nathanael (also called Bartholomew), Thomas, Simon, Judas, and James (son of Alphaeus).

#3

The apostles were good examples for all to follow. They tried to be like Jesus.

They followed in his footsteps and tried to keep the commandments. They knew that obeying the commandments would bring them closer to Jesus and to Heavenly Father.

Jesus said, "*He that hath my commandments, and keepeth them, he it is that loveth me: and he that loveth me shall be loved of my Father, and I will love him, and will manifest [show] myself to him*" (John 14:21).

FILE FOLDER SHOW-AND-TELL:

#4 Thousands of people followed Jesus and the apostles from Galilee, Jerusalem, Judea, and beyond Jordan. They heard of his teachings and miracles.

Jesus wanted the apostles to teach others about the gospel of Jesus Christ. He said to Simon Peter, *"I have prayed for thee, that thy faith fail not: and when thou art converted, strengthen thy brethren"* (Luke 22:32).

He said: *"Go ye therefore, and teach all nations, baptizing them in the name of the Father, and of the Son, and of the Holy Ghost: Teaching them to observe all things whatsoever I have commanded you: and, lo, I am with you alway[s], even unto the end of the world"* (Matthew 28:19-20).

The apostles were not alone in their missionary assignments. Jesus guided them while he was on the earth, and sent the Comforter, or Holy Ghost, when he left.

#5 The apostles were special witnesses of Jesus. They shared their testimony of his life and teachings with others.

The first four books of the New Testament were written by four witnesses—the apostles Matthew, Mark, Luke, and John. The apostles told Christ's story, from his birth to his death and resurrection. They told how they were called by him to be fishers of men. They were proud to be his friends.

They told of the miracles he performed--when he calmed the seas, walked on water, and fed the 5,000 with only five loaves of bread and two fish. How did he do these things? He had the priesthood, the power of God.
He healed the sick and raised others from the dead.

#6 When it came time for him to be crucified, Jesus knew what would happen.   He told the apostles, *"Yet a little while, and the world seeth me no more; but ye see me: because I live, ye shall live also"* (John 14:19).

He knew the apostles loved him, and he loved the apostles. Because they loved him, they were sad that he was leaving.

He told them he would send a special spirit to guide them. Jesus said: *"The Comforter, which is the Holy Ghost, ... shall teach you all things, and bring all things to your remembrance"* (John 14:26).

This comforter is an anchor in our lives. A boat needs an anchor to keep it from moving into dangerous waters. If we listen to the still, small voice, it will keep us from danger by teaching us truths and giving us guidance.

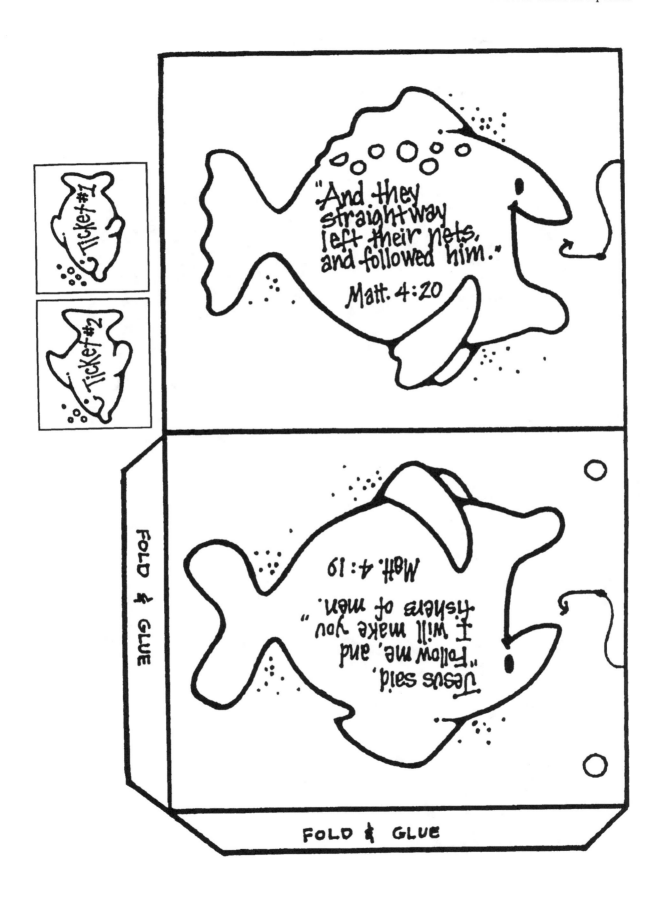

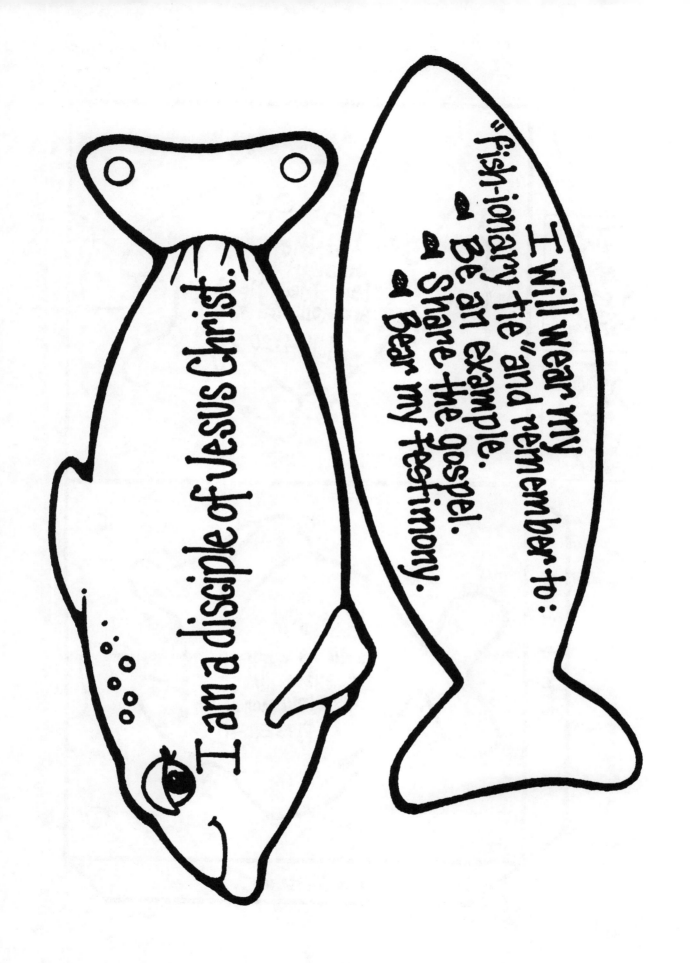

I am a disciple of Jesus Christ.

"I will wear my "fish-ionary tie" and remember to:
- Be an example.
- Share the gospel.
- Bear my testimony.

File Folder FAMILY HOME EVENING
BLESSED BEATITUDES:
Jesus Gave the Sermon on the Mount

SONG: "Tell Me the Stories of Jesus," page 57 in the *Children's Songbook**.

INTRODUCTION:

Say, "Let's get an attitude towards the beatitudes that Jesus gave during his Sermon on the Mount. The beatitudes tell us how we can do to get to heaven. They tell us how we can be happy, like *Blessed are the pure in heart: for they shall see God"* (Matthew 5:8).

"Jesus gave nine blessings in Matthew 5:3-12. They all start with a good attitude. Think as Jesus thought. Think of the happiness that can come from living his teachings."

"Remember: You can't <u>beat</u> a good <u>attitude</u>, so BE A BEE-ATITUDE BELIEVER."

SEEDS OF FAITH:
My Testimony Is Growing
FILE FOLDER SHOW-AND-TELL:
CREATE: Cut out cue cards (pages 50-51) and file folder label (page iii). Color and cut out visuals (pages 52-53). Glue the label on file folder.
PRESENT: Read cue cards and place visuals on folder with tape or Velcro.

ACTIVITY: Bee-atitude Blockbuster quiz game. Learn the beatitudes by guessing the missing words written on beatitude blocks. **To Make:** (1) Copy, color and cut out Block Buster blocks (pages 54-55).

(2) Fold and glue edges, and tape down lid. **To Play:** (1) Divide into two teams. (2) Take turns rolling one block at a time, alternating blocks. (3) Play for points.
THE FIRST TO EARN 100 POINTS WINS:
❑ **10 POINTS:** Land on Bee-atitude Blessing and find the missing word in the scriptures. ❑ **20 POINTS:** Guess the missing word. ❑ **20 POINTS:** Land on Bee-atitude Blockbuster.
❑ **20 POINTS:** Land on Buzz Your Way to Heaven.

THOUGHT TREATS:
Honey Buzz Taffy and Bee-atitude Bagels
(details on page 112-113).

FILE FOLDER SHOW-AND-TELL:

#1 <u>Blessed Beatitudes: Jesus Gave the Sermon on the Mount</u>.
♥ One day, Jesus taught thousands of people at one time. This was called the Sermon on the Mount. He told the people how they could get to heaven. He gave them the beatitudes and other words of wisdom.
The beatitudes tell us how to be perfect. Each has a blessing that comes from obedience.
♥ Jesus said, *"Be ye therefore perfect, even as your Father which is in Heaven is perfect"* (Matthew 5:48*)*. Jesus taught us to BEE PERFECT, so let's build a beehive and learn to bee-have, so we can buzz to heaven's beehive. Let these bees tell you how being a Beatitude Believer can buzz you closer to heaven.

#2 ♥ I am **Poor in Spirit Bee**. I am looking for the kingdom of heaven.
Jesus told me: *"Blessed are the poor in spirit [who come unto me*], for theirs is the kingdom of heaven"* (Matthew 5:3; *3 Nephi 12:3). Jesus said that if I am poor in spirit, and I come unto him, then I will be a part of his kingdom.   **I WILL LISTEN AND "BEE" AS JESUS
WOULD HAVE ME "BEE".**

#3 ♥ I am called **Mourning Bee**. Mourn means to be sad. I am sad, and I am looking for comfort.
♥ Jesus told me: *"Blessed are they that mourn: for they shall be comforted."*
It feels so nice to know that I have a loving Father in
Heaven who wishes to care for me.
**I BUZZ LOVE AND COMFORT TO OTHERS,
AS HEAVENLY FATHER COMFORTS ME.**

#4 ♥ I am known as **Meek Bee**. I try to be gentle with others. I am long-suffering, patient, and tolerant.
♥ Jesus promised me, saying: *"Blessed are the meek: for they shall inherit the earth."* This means that I will have many blessings while I am
on this earth. This is true, as I have many blessings.
**I WILL "BEE" LONG-SUFFERING, BUZZ KIND
WORDS, "BEE" PATIENT, AND TRY TO UNDERSTAND.**

#5 ♥ I am **Righteous Bee**. I try to choose the right each day. I help my neighbor and I pray.
♥ Jesus said: "Blessed are they which do hunger and thirst after righteousness: for they shall be filled [with the Holy Ghost*]" (Matthew 5:6; *3 Nephi 12:6).
I have a strong desire to read the scriptures each day, so I can learn the
righteous way.
I WILL "BEE" GOOD.

#6 ♥ I am **Merciful Bee**. I am thoughtful of others. If someone is hurt, I try to help them. I have what you call compassion. I feel sorry for those who are in need, and help where I can.
♥ Jesus promised me, saying: "Blessed are the merciful: for they shall obtain mercy" (Matthew 5:7). This means that if I show kindness to others, someone will be kind to me when I am in need.
I WILL BUZZ OVER TO HELP SOMEONE.

FILE FOLDER SHOW-AND-TELL:

#7

♥ I am **Pure in Heart Bee**. My friends call me the straight arrow, because I like to do precisely the right thing. My thoughts are honest, and my actions are straightforward. You know what I am thinking and doing.
♥ Jesus said: *"Blessed are the pure in heart: for they shall see God"* (Matthew 5:8). I'm trying to be like Jesus.

LET'S BUZZ ALONG THE STRAIGHT AND NARROW PATH.

#8

♥ I am **Peacemaker Bee**. Whenever there is fighting, or someone hurts someone else, I am there to help them feel calm. I try to find out what the problem is, and get help.
♥ Jesus promised me, saying: *"Blessed are the peacemakers: for they shall be called the children of God"* (Matthew 5:9).

I WILL "BEE" PEACEFUL WITH MY FAMILY AND FRIENDS, AND "BEE" A GOOD NEIGHBOR.

#9

♥ I am **Persecuted for the Right Bee**. I try to do what is right, and make right choices. Sometimes others are mean to me and treat me bad. They say I should be doing the things they are doing. But those things are not right.
♥ Jesus said: *"Blessed are they which are persecuted for righteousness' sake: for theirs is the kingdom of heaven"* (Matthew 5:10). I know that my reward will be in heaven, and not always on this earth.

I WILL BUZZ "NO" TO WRONG CHOICES.

#10

♥ I am called **Light Bee**. I try to shine brightly. I do not hide my light. I let it shine, so others can see that I am a good worker bee. When they see good works, they can feel closer to heaven's beehive.
♥ Jesus said: *"Ye are the light of the world ... Light a candle ... on a candlestick ... Let your light so shine ..."* (Matthew 5:14-16).

I WILL BUZZ BRIGHT TOWARD HEAVEN'S LIGHT.

#11

♥ I am called **Teacher Bee**. I teach others to do what is right. Jesus said that we should <u>not</u> teach others to break these commandments. He said: *"Whosoever ... shall break one of these ... commandments, and shall teach men so, he shall be called the least in the kingdom of heaven: but whosoever shall do and TEACH them, the same shall be called GREAT in the kingdom of heaven"* (Matthew 5:19).
♥ This means if I encourage my friends to do wrong, then I am teaching them wrong, and I will not have a high place in the beehive on high. I must teach them to do right.

I WILL BUZZ A MESSAGE TO OTHERS TO CHOOSE THE RIGHT.

#12

♥ I am **Love Bee**. I love everyone, even my enemies. Jesus said: *"Love your enemies, bless them that curse you, do good to them that hate you, and pray for them which despitefully use you, and persecute you; that ye may be the children of your Father which is in heaven"* (Matthew 5:44-45).

I WILL LOVE OTHERS AS JESUS DID, AND BUZZ TO MY HEAVENLY HIVE.

 -ATITUDE
BLESSING
"Blessed are they
which are persecuted for
righteousness' sake: for
theirs is the kingdom
of _____."
(Matt. 5:10)

HEAVEN!!
BUZZ YOUR WAY TO

 -ATITUDE
BLESSING
"Blessed are
the meek: for
they shall inherit
the _____"
(Matt. 5:5)

-ANTUDE
BLESSING
"Blessed are
they which do hunger
and thirst after
righteousness: for
they shall be_____"
(Matt.5:6)

-ATITUDE
BLESSING
"Blessed are
they that mourn:
for they shall be
_____"
(Matt: 5:4)

BUSTER

54

 -ATITUDE BLESSING "Blessed are the pure in heart: for they shall ___ ___ God." (Matt. 5:8)

 HEAVEN! BUZZ YOUR WAY TO

 -ATITUDE BLESSING "Blessed are the merciful: for they shall obtain ___ ___ ___." (Matt. 5:7)

-ATITUDE BLESSING "Blessed are the peacemakers: for they shall be called the ___ ___ ___ of ___ ___ ___" (Matt. 5:9)

 -ATITUDE BLESSING "Blessed are the poor in spirit: for theirs is the Kingdom of ___ ___ ___." (Matt. 5:3)

 BLESSER BUSTER

File Folder FAMILY HOME EVENING
THE GIFTS HE GAVE: Tell Me the Stories of Jesus

SONG: "Tell Me the Stories of Jesus," page 57 in the
Children's Songbook*.

INTRODUCTION:

Tell family, "At Christmas time, we honor the birth of Jesus by giving gifts to others. By giving gifts, we show our love for others and for Jesus. Jesus showed love for us by giving gifts that we can enjoy all year. These gifts are the stories he told. They are called parables. The apostles recorded them, and we can find them in the books of the New Testament. Let's learn about the gifts he gave. Tell me the stories of Jesus."

THE GIFTS HE GAVE:

Tell Me the Stories of Jesus

File Folder Show-and-Tell:

CREATE: Cut out cue cards (pages 57-58) and file folder label (page iii). Color and cut out visuals (pages 59-62). Glue the label on file folder.

PRESENT: Read cue cards and place visuals on folder with tape or Velcro.

ACTIVITY: Parables in a Pocket: Tell Me the Stories of Jesus match game (shown left). See page 63 for details.

THOUGHT TREAT: Idea #1 <u>Unforgettable Parable Cupcakes</u> (shown right). See page 113 for details.
Idea #2 <u>Gift Cookie</u> (shown below). See page 113 for details.

*Children's Songbook is published by The Church of Jesus Christ of Latter-day Saints, Salt Lake City, Utah.

FILE FOLDER SHOW-AND-TELL:

#1 **THE GIFTS HE GAVE: Tell Me the Stories of Jesus**
Jesus was a great teacher. He taught in parables,
or stories. Each parable will tell you how you can get to heaven.

Parable of the Lost Sheep: There was a good shepherd who had
100 sheep. One day, when he counted the sheep, one was lost. He
counted only 99 sheep, so he went out to look for the lost one.
He wanted to save it from the wolves and from starving.

He searched until he found it. He was happy as he picked it up and
carried it home on his shoulders. When he got home, he told his friends
and neighbors that he found the lost lamb.

Jesus told the Pharisees that this story was about him. He is like the good shepherd, and sinners are
like the lost sheep. Jesus said he came to save the lost sheep, to save people from their sins.

Jesus has told us he is very happy when he finds sinners who repent.
JESUS WANTS US TO FIND AND HELP THOSE IN NEED.

#2 **Parable of the Talents:** A man had three servants. He gave
each servant some money. Each coin was called a talent.

He gave the first servant <u>five</u> talents, and the second servant <u>two</u>
talents, and to the third servant he gave <u>one</u> talent. Each servant went their
way.

The first servant with <u>five</u> talents worked hard and earned <u>five</u> more
talents. He had <u>ten</u> talents to bring back.

The second servant with <u>two</u> talents worked hard and earned <u>two</u> more
talents. He had <u>four</u> talents to bring back.

The third servant was afraid he would lose the <u>one</u> talent he was given, so
he buried it in the ground. When it was time to go back, he dug it up and brought back the <u>one</u> talent
he was given.

When the servants reported back to the man who gave them the talents, the man was happy. The
two servants had worked hard and increased their talents, so he gave them more talents.
He was angry with the third servant who buried his talent. He took his talent away and gave it to
another. Then he sent the lazy servant away.
JESUS WANTS US TO WORK HARD TO INCREASE OUR TALENTS.

#3 **Ten Young Women:** Ten young women were going to
help at a wedding. Five women were wise, and they took
extra oil to light their lamps. The other five were foolish.
They did not take extra oil in case their lamps went out.

They all waited for the bridegroom to let them in. It was late,
and they fell asleep. At midnight it was time to go in.

The five women who were wise had enough oil to light their
lamps, but the five who were foolish could not light their lamps.
They had to leave to buy more oil.

While they were gone, the wedding began. The five wise women
were allowed to go in, but the five foolish women were late and the
doors were closed.

Jesus is like the bridegroom, and we are like these young women.
JESUS WANTS US TO BE PREPARED, AS HE WILL COME AGAIN.

FILE FOLDER SHOW-AND-TELL:

#4 **Parable of the Lost Son:** A man had two sons who would receive his money when he died. The younger son wanted his money now.

The father gave the younger son the money. The son left home and sinned. He did not obey God's commandments. He spent all his money, and had no money to buy food.

He found a job feeding pigs, and was so hungry, he wanted to eat the food the pigs were eating. He thought of his family and their food. He knew he had sinned, but he wanted to go home. He went home to repent and ask his father to forgive him.

His father saw him coming and threw his arms around him and kissed him. The son told his father that he was sorry for not obeying him, and for not obeying God. The father had his servants bring the boy new clothes, shoes, and a ring for his finger. He had a big dinner for his son to tell everyone how happy he was that his son was home.

The older son was angry, and told the father that he had obeyed him; yet, he had never received a special dinner in his honor. The father told the older son that everything he had would belong to him someday. But the younger son had gone away and come home again; he was a sinner and had repented. **JESUS WANTS US TO REPENT AND TO FORGIVE OTHERS.**

#5 **Parable of the Mustard Seed:** The ruler of the Jerusalem synagogue, or church, asked Jesus, "What is the kingdom of God like?" Jesus said: *"It is like a grain of mustard seed, which a man took, and cast into his garden; and it grew, and waxed a great tree; and the fowls of the air lodged in the branches of it"* (Luke 13:18).

We too can be like this man who planted a mustard seed. We can plant good thoughts in our minds as we read the scriptures. We can grow as we keep the commandments.

Jesus also said that the mustard seed *"is the least of all seeds: but when it is grown, it is the greatest among herbs"* (Matthew 13:32).

We can grow with good thoughts and good deeds, like the mustard seed. We can grow tall in spirit as well as stature, like the seed that grew into a 10-15 foot tree. **JESUS WANTS US TO PLANT GOOD THOUGHTS AND GROW TOWARD HEAVEN.**

#6 **Parable of the Good Samaritan:** A leader of the Jews asked Jesus how to get to heaven. Jesus asked him what the scriptures said. The man said to love God and love your neighbor. Jesus said he was right. Then the leader asked Jesus, "Who is my neighbor?"

Jesus told the story of a Jew walking along the road. Some thieves stopped him, beat him, and took his clothes. The Jewish man was left along the road, almost dead.

A Jewish priest came by and saw that the man was hurt, yet he passed by, leaving him alone.

A Levite man came by and saw that he was hurt, but he walked by on the other side of the road, leaving him alone.

Then a Samaritan man came along. Samaritans and Jews did not get along. The Samaritan knew the man was a Jew, but he stopped to help him. He put clothes on the man and took him to an inn, and took care of him until the next day. When he left, he gave money to the man in the inn to take care of him. **JESUS WANTS US TO BE KIND TO OTHERS AND HELP THEM.** These are just a few of the gifts Jesus gave. Let's search the scriptures to find more stories and blessings from Jesus.

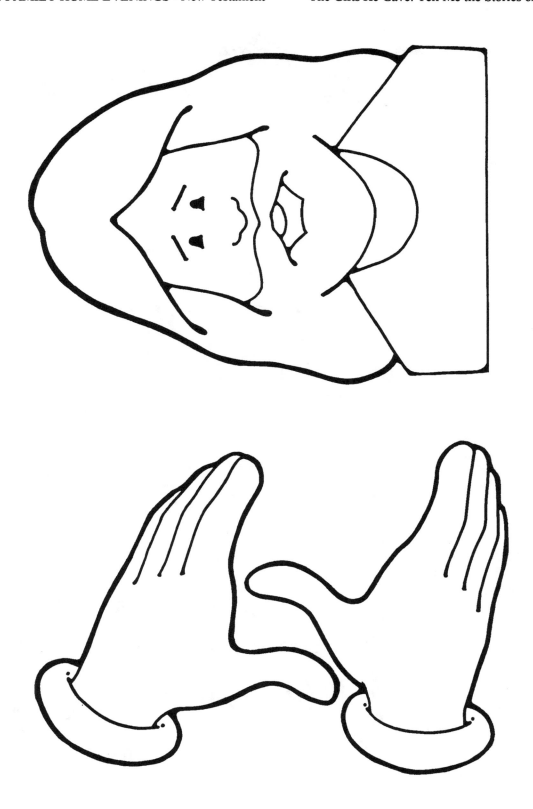

PATTERN: Gift #1
PARABLE: The Lost
Sheep for Scripture
Show-and-Tell

♥ Copy on cardstock
paper (one set for Show-
and-Tell and one set for
Parables in a Pocket
game).

PATTERN: Gift #2
PARABLE: The Talents for
Scripture Show-and-Tell
♥ Copy on cardstock paper.

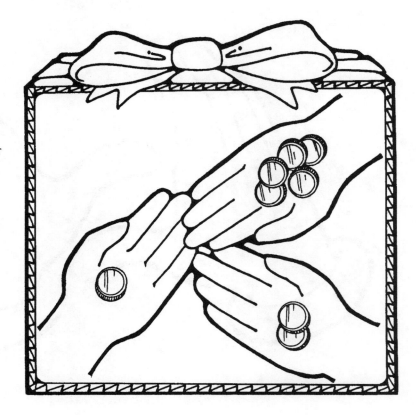

PATTERN: Gift #3
PARABLE: Ten Young
Women for Scripture
Show-and-Tell
♥ Copy on cardstock
paper.

PATTERN: Gift #4
PARABLE: The Lost Son
for Scripture Show-
and-Tell
♥ Copy on cardstock
paper.

PATTERN: Gift #5
PARABLE: The
Mustard Seed for
Scripture Show-and-Tell

♥ Copy on cardstock
paper.

PATTERN: Gift #6
PARABLE: The Good
Samaritan for Scripture
Show-and-Tell
♥ Copy on cardstock
paper.

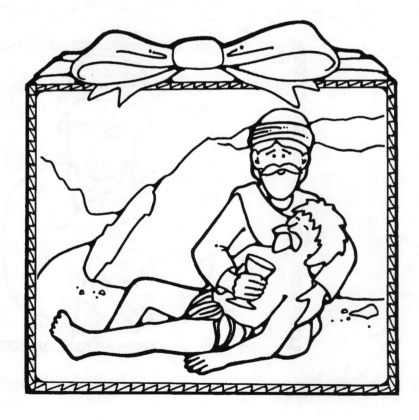

ACTIVITY: Parables in a Pocket: Tell Me the Stories of Jesus Match Game

OBJECTIVE: Mix up the parable wordstrips and place in the right parable (gift) pocket. Tell family to listen carefully to the Show-and-Tell presentation so they will know the answers to play this fun match game. Enjoy reading each completed parable together.

YOU'LL NEED: Copies of Parables in a Pocket sign and wordstrips (pages 64-67), and gifts (pages 60-62), a file folder, glue, and markers.

HOW TO MAKE GAME BOARD & GAME:

1. Color and cut out gift pictures, Parables in a Pocket sign, and wordstrips #1-6.
2. Glue gifts to the inside of a file folder 1/4" on sides and bottom, leaving the top open to create a pocket.

HOW TO PLAY GAME:

1. <u>Mix parable wordstrips</u> #1-6 from each parable in a bowl or box to draw from.
2. <u>Divide into two teams</u> with two players from each team helping each other.
3. <u>Match a Parable</u>: Team players take turns drawing a parable wordstrip, reading it, and placing it in the matching parable pocket.
4. <u>Read Parables in Pocket</u>: As soon as wordstrips #1-6 are placed in a pocket, the
pocket is full. The team that placed the last wordstrip pulls out wordstrips #1-6 and reads the parable aloud. If time permits, play until all parables are read.

PATTERN: Parables in a Pocket game

PATTERN: Parables in a Pocket game (Parables: The Lost Sheep and The Talents)

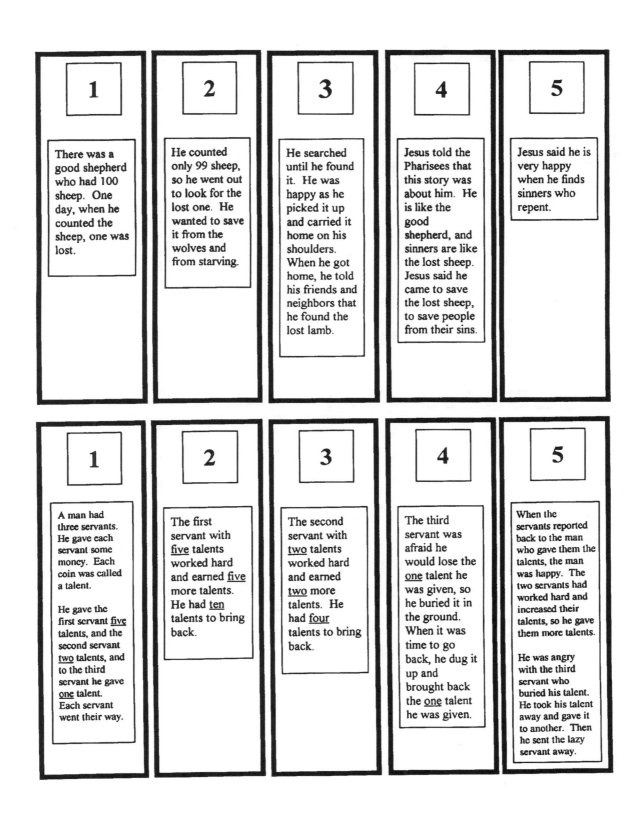

1

There was a good shepherd who had 100 sheep. One day, when he counted the sheep, one was lost.

2

He counted only 99 sheep, so he went out to look for the lost one. He wanted to save it from the wolves and from starving.

3

He searched until he found it. He was happy as he picked it up and carried it home on his shoulders. When he got home, he told his friends and neighbors that he found the lost lamb.

4

Jesus told the Pharisees that this story was about him. He is like the good shepherd, and sinners are like the lost sheep. Jesus said he came to save the lost sheep, to save people from their sins.

5

Jesus said he is very happy when he finds sinners who repent.

1

A man had three servants. He gave each servant some money. Each coin was called a talent.

He gave the first servant five talents, and the second servant two talents, and to the third servant he gave one talent. Each servant went their way.

2

The first servant with five talents worked hard and earned five more talents. He had ten talents to bring back.

3

The second servant with two talents worked hard and earned two more talents. He had four talents to bring back.

4

The third servant was afraid he would lose the one talent he was given, so he buried it in the ground. When it was time to go back, he dug it up and brought back the one talent he was given.

5

When the servants reported back to the man who gave them the talents, the man was happy. The two servants had worked hard and increased their talents, so he gave them more talents.

He was angry with the third servant who buried his talent. He took his talent away and gave it to another. Then he sent the lazy servant away.

PATTERN: Parables in a Pocket game (Parables: Ten Young Women and The Lost Son)

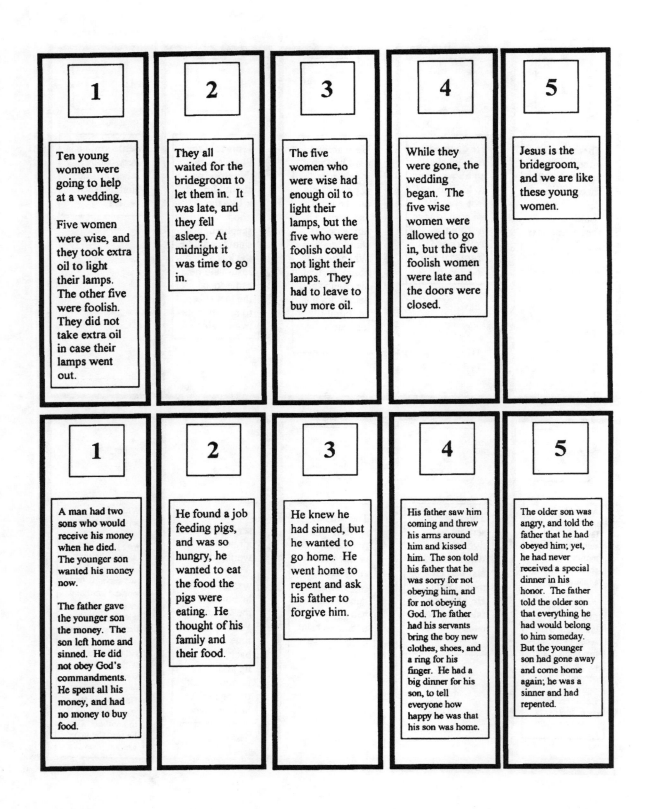

1 Ten young women were going to help at a wedding.

Five women were wise, and they took extra oil to light their lamps. The other five were foolish. They did not take extra oil in case their lamps went out.

2 They all waited for the bridegroom to let them in. It was late, and they fell asleep. At midnight it was time to go in.

3 The five women who were wise had enough oil to light their lamps, but the five who were foolish could not light their lamps. They had to leave to buy more oil.

4 While they were gone, the wedding began. The five wise women were allowed to go in, but the five foolish women were late and the doors were closed.

5 Jesus is the bridegroom, and we are like these young women.

1 A man had two sons who would receive his money when he died. The younger son wanted his money now.

The father gave the younger son the money. The son left home and sinned. He did not obey God's commandments. He spent all his money, and had no money to buy food.

2 He found a job feeding pigs, and was so hungry, he wanted to eat the food the pigs were eating. He thought of his family and their food.

3 He knew he had sinned, but he wanted to go home. He went home to repent and ask his father to forgive him.

4 His father saw him coming and threw his arms around him and kissed him. The son told his father that he was sorry for not obeying him, and for not obeying God. The father had his servants bring the boy new clothes, shoes, and a ring for his finger. He had a big dinner for his son, to tell everyone how happy he was that his son was home.

5 The older son was angry, and told the father that he had obeyed him; yet, he had never received a special dinner in his honor. The father told the older son that everything he had would belong to him someday. But the younger son had gone away and come home again; he was a sinner and had repented.

PATTERN: Parables in a Pocket game (Parables: The Mustard Seed and The Good Samaritan)

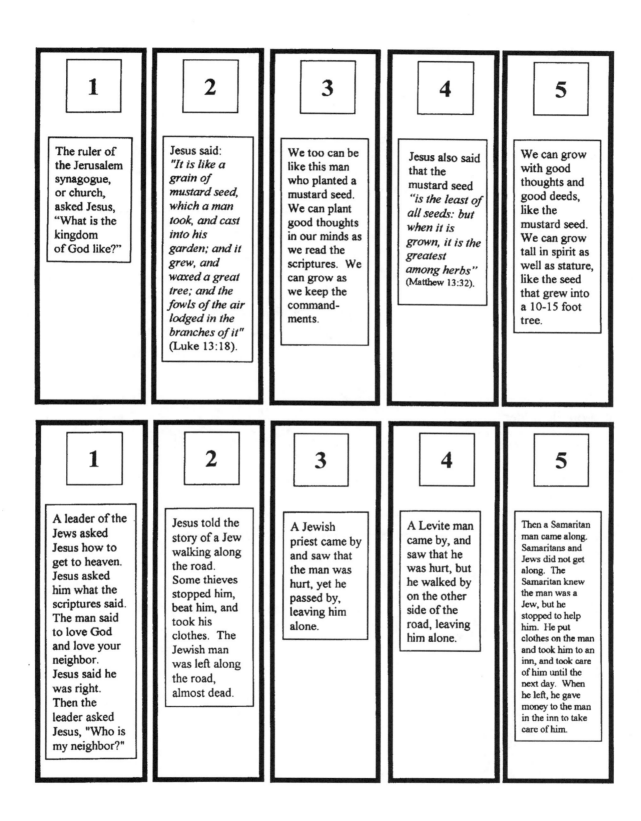

1 The ruler of the Jerusalem synagogue, or church, asked Jesus, "What is the kingdom of God like?"

2 Jesus said: *"It is like a grain of mustard seed, which a man took, and cast into his garden; and it grew, and waxed a great tree; and the fowls of the air lodged in the branches of it"* (Luke 13:18).

3 We too can be like this man who planted a mustard seed. We can plant good thoughts in our minds as we read the scriptures. We can grow as we keep the commandments.

4 Jesus also said that the mustard seed *"is the least of all seeds: but when it is grown, it is the greatest among herbs"* (Matthew 13:32).

5 We can grow with good thoughts and good deeds, like the mustard seed. We can grow tall in spirit as well as stature, like the seed that grew into a 10-15 foot tree.

1 A leader of the Jews asked Jesus how to get to heaven. Jesus asked him what the scriptures said. The man said to love God and love your neighbor. Jesus said he was right. Then the leader asked Jesus, "Who is my neighbor?"

2 Jesus told the story of a Jew walking along the road. Some thieves stopped him, beat him, and took his clothes. The Jewish man was left along the road, almost dead.

3 A Jewish priest came by and saw that the man was hurt, yet he passed by, leaving him alone.

4 A Levite man came by, and saw that he was hurt, but he walked by on the other side of the road, leaving him alone.

5 Then a Samaritan man came along. Samaritans and Jews did not get along. The Samaritan knew the man was a Jew, but he stopped to help him. He put clothes on the man and took him to an inn, and took care of him until the next day. When he left, he gave money to the man in the inn to take care of him.

File Folder FAMILY HOME EVENING

SERVICE WITH A SMILE: Jesus Performed Miracles

OPENING SONG: "I Feel My Savior's Love," page 74 in the *Children's Songbook**.

INTRODUCTION:

Tell family, "Let's follow Jesus and learn how to show SERVICE WITH A SMILE. Jesus came to earth to show us how to help others. He healed the sick, calmed the seas, walked on water, and cured lepers of disease. Let's follow the path that Jesus walked; let's not just sit and talk. He led the way, he walked that mile; he showed us SERVICE WITH A SMILE."

SERVICE WITH A SMILE: Jesus Performed Miracles
File Folder Show-and-Tell

CREATE: Cut out cue cards (pages 69-70) and file folder label (page iii). Color and cut out visuals (pages 71-72). Glue the label on file folder.

PRESENT: Read cue cards and place visuals on folder with tape or Velcro.

ACTIVITY: Go the Extra Mile: Show Service with a Smile match game. See page 73 for details.

THOUGHT TREAT: <u>Chip in and Help! Potato Chips</u> (shown right). See page 114 for details.

**Children's Songbook* is published by The Church of Jesus Christ of Latter-day Saints, Salt Lake City, Utah.

FILE FOLDER SHOW-AND-TELL:

#1

SERVICE WITH A SMILE: Jesus Performed Miracles

Jesus showed us how to show service with a smile. Heavenly Father sent his son Jesus to the earth to show us the way back to heaven. Jesus taught the people, healed the sick, and performed many other miracles.

Jesus held the priesthood, the power to act in God's name to work these miracles. Because Jesus was obedient to Heavenly Father, he was able to help and serve others.

He went the second mile to do good works. By his miracles and teachings we know that he is the Son of God.

Jesus Healed a Man Who Could Not Walk. There was a man who could not walk. He was carried to where Jesus was teaching and healing the people. So many people had come to see Jesus. The man who was in the bed could not get close to Jesus. So his friends cut a hole in the roof and lowered him down into the house with ropes. Jesus saw their faith and said unto him, "Man, thy sins are forgiven thee ... Arise, and take up thy couch, and go into thine house. And immediately he rose up ... and departed to his own house, glorifying God" (Luke 5:17-25).

#2

Jesus Commanded the Wind and the Waves.

Jesus and his disciples were on a boat in the Sea of Galilee. Jesus fell asleep and the wind began to blow hard. The waves were high and the boat filled with water. The disciples woke Jesus. They were afraid the boat would sink.

They asked Jesus to help. He stood up and commanded the wind to stop blowing and the waves to calm down. When everything was calm, Jesus asked the disciples why they were afraid. He told them they should have more faith.

His disciples were amazed and wondered what kind of man he was that he could stop the wind and calm the waves. The wind and the waves obeyed Jesus. Why did Jesus have such a power? Because of his faith.

#3

Jesus Fed 5,000 People.

More than 5,000 people followed Jesus near the Sea of Galilee. Jesus taught the people all day, telling them of Heavenly Father's plan.

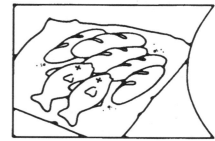

When it was night, the disciples told Jesus that the people were hungry and they should go home and eat. There was not enough food to feed 5,000 people. There were only five loaves of bread and two fish.

Then, a wonderful thing happened. Jesus told the people to sit down. Then he blessed the bread and fish and fed the 5,000 people. They all had enough to eat, and there were baskets of food left over. The people were amazed that Jesus had performed this miracle.

FILE FOLDER SHOW-AND-TELL

#4   **Jesus Walked on Water.**

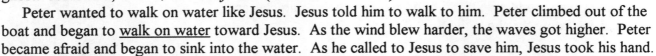

When Jesus went to the mountain to pray, his disciples went out to the Sea of Galilee on a boat. A big storm came; the winds were blowing hard, and the waves were high. Jesus came down from the mountain and walked on water to get to the boat.

His disciples saw him and were afraid, thinking he was a ghost. Jesus said, *"It is I; be not afraid"* (Matthew 14:26-27).

Peter wanted to walk on water like Jesus. Jesus told him to walk to him. Peter climbed out of the boat and began to walk on water toward Jesus. As the wind blew harder, the waves got higher. Peter became afraid and began to sink into the water. As he called to Jesus to save him, Jesus took his hand.

Jesus asked Peter why he was afraid. He asked him why he did not have more faith. Jesus and Peter then walked to the boat, and the storm stopped. His disciples honored and worshipped Jesus. They had a testimony that he was the Son of God.

#5   **Jesus Raised Lazarus from the Dead.**

Lazarus lived in Bethany. He and his sisters, Martha and Mary, loved Jesus.

Lazarus became very sick and his sister sent for Jesus. Jesus told the disciples Lazarus was dead. He told them he would bring Lazarus back to life. This way, they would know he was the true Savior.

When Jesus came, Lazarus had been dead four days. Jesus asked his sister Martha if she believed that he could make Lazarus live again. Martha said yes. They opened the grave of Lazarus, and Jesus prayed to Heavenly Father. Jesus told Lazarus to come to life again, and Lazarus came out of the grave alive.

The people knew Jesus was the Savior. They knew Heavenly Father had sent him. They had a testimony. They believed that Jesus was God's Son.

#6   **Jesus Healed Ten Lepers.**

Jesus went to a small town, where he saw ten very sick men. They were lepers. They had large sores all over their bodies. Their skin was falling off. Doctors could not help them. The people stayed away from them so they would not get sick. The lepers were in great pain.

The ten lepers asked Jesus to heal them. They had faith that Jesus could make their sores go away. Jesus wanted them to be well, and told them to go the priests. The lepers obeyed Jesus and went to the priests. On their way, the ten lepers were healed. Their sores were all gone.

Only one of the lepers came back to thank Jesus. He knelt down before him and thanked him for making him well. Jesus said that his faith had made him well. The other lepers did not come back to thank Jesus.

JESUS PERFORMED MIRACLES TO SHOW US THE POWER OF THE PRIESTHOOD, AND TO TEACH US TO HAVE MORE FAITH IN HIM AND IN HEAVENLY FATHER.

Jesus said: *"No man can do these miracles ... except God be with him"* (John 3:2).

How can we thank Jesus for all these miracles? **We can show SERVICE WITH A SMILE.**

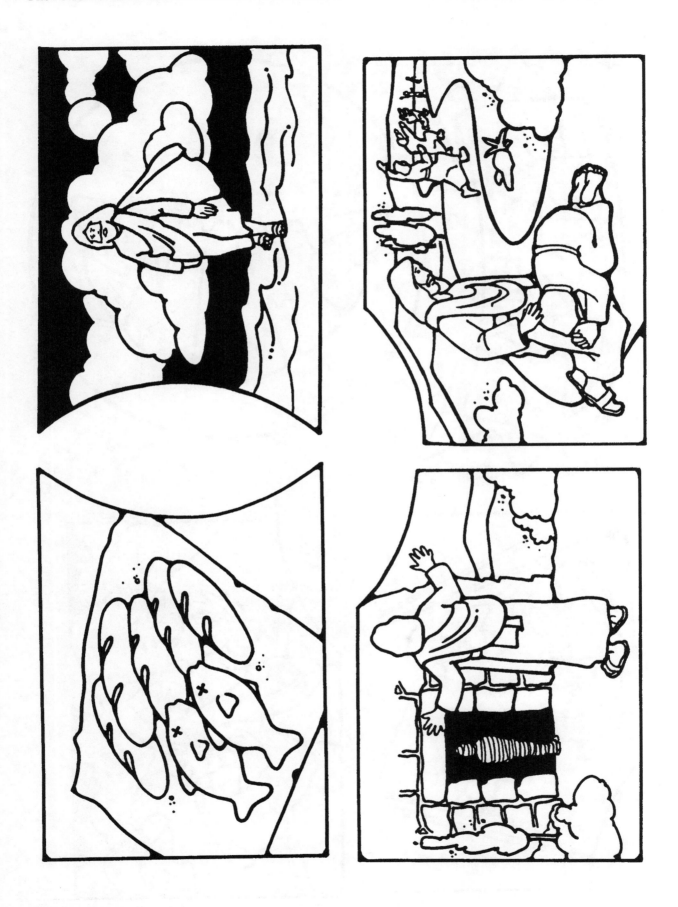

ACTIVITY: Go the Extra Mile: Show Service with a Smile match game

OBJECTIVE: Learn fun ways to serve others with a smile.

YOU'LL NEED: One or two copies of match card sets (pages 74-75) on colored cardstock paper, scissors, and crayons or markers.

TO MAKE GAME: Color and cut out cards.

TO PLAY:
1. Place word cards on the left and picture cards on the right face down on the floor or table.
2. Mix up cards in their separate piles.
3. Take turns picking up two cards to see if you can make a match.

CAUTION: Be careful! These dual match cards may fool you, e.g. "I can talk to and water ..." card can match with "Dad's shoes." Would you really want to water Dad's shoes? Or, would a better match be to water "... the plants"?

Have fun with this one. You are sure to discover SERVICE WITH A SMILE!

PATTERN: Go the Extra Mile: Show Service with a Smile match game

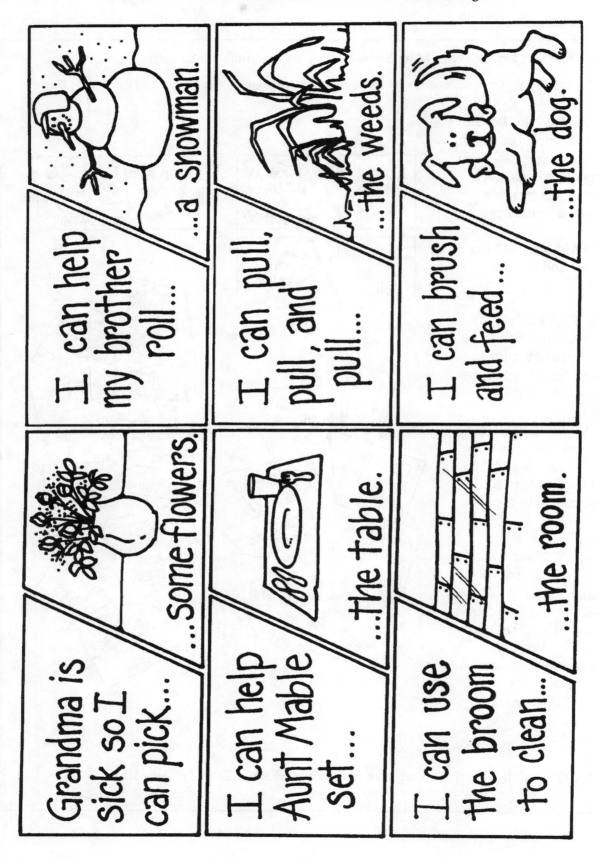

PATTERN: Go the Extra Mile: Show Service with a Smile match game

...some cookies.

...the plants.

...Dad's shoes.

I can make and bake for a friend...

I can talk to and water...

I can clean and polish...

...the dishes.

...the trash.

...the baby.

I can dry and put away...

I can pick up and pack out...

I can change and watch...

CHOOSE THE RIGHT: Jesus Is Our Light

SONGS: "Choose the Right Way," page 160, "Teach Me to Walk in the Light," page 177, or "Jesus Wants Me For a Sunbeam," page 160 in the Children's Songbook*.

INTRODUCTION:

Tell family, "Jesus was sent to us to be our light. He showed us the way to light and happiness. He said: *"Ye are the light of the world ... Let your light so shine"* (Matthew 5:14, 16). We can keep heaven in sight as we Choose the Right. Our life can be a happy circle: The more you choose the right, the happier you become. The happier you become, the more your light shines."

CHOOSE THE RIGHT:
Jesus Is Our Light
FILE FOLDER
SHOW-AND-TELL:

CREATE: Cut out cue cards (pages 77-78) and file folder label (page iii). Color and cut out visuals (pages 79-80). Glue the label on file folder.
PRESENT: Read cue cards and place visuals on folder with tape or Velcro.

ACTIVITY: CHOOSE THE RIGHT: Red Light, Green Light (detailed on page 81).

PRIZES: "Souper" Choice soup can filled with Choose The Right motivational word-strips, and Choose the Right: Jesus Is Our Light light switch cover (pages 81, 83-85).

THOUGHT TREAT:
Choo Choose the Right soda cracker train. See details on page 114.

Children's Songbook is published by The Church of Jesus Christ of Latter-day Saints, Salt Lake City, Utah.

FILE FOLDER SHOW-AND-TELL:

#1 **CHOOSE THE RIGHT: Jesus Is Our Light**

Heavenly Father Sent His Son: Jesus Is Our Light.

The light of Jesus Christ is given to all people to help them choose the right.

Jesus said that we are the light of the world. We are not to hide our light under a bushel, but put it on a candlestick so that others may see. He said:

"Let your light so shine before men, that they may see your good works, and glorify your Father which is in heaven" (Matthew 5:14-16).

When we let our light shine, we are showing honor and thanks to our Heavenly Father.

Jesus was sent to the earth to light the way to happiness. He is the light we must follow. We are here to learn how to CHOOSE THE RIGHT.

HERE ARE SOME WAYS WE CAN LET OUR LIGHT SHINE AS JESUS DID:

#2 **Choose the Right by Loving Others as Jesus Did.**

When the apostles were with Jesus, some people wanted Jesus to bless their children. The apostles told the people not to bring their children to Jesus, because he was tired.

"But when Jesus saw it, he was much displeased, and said unto them, Suffer the little children to come unto me, and forbid them not: for of such is the kingdom of God" (Mark 10:14).

Jesus loved the little children. He knew they were all Heavenly Father's children. The children loved Jesus. He was kind and listened to them. He blessed them. We can love others as Jesus did.

#3 **Choose the Right by Being Baptized as Jesus Was Baptized.**

Jesus went to John the Baptist, who was baptizing people in the Jordan River. John knew that Jesus was righteous, that he had always obeyed Heavenly Father's commandments. Jesus did not need to repent or to have his sins washed away, but he knew that God commanded everyone to be baptized.

"But John forbad him, saying, I have need to be baptized of thee, and comest thou to me?" (Matthew 3:14)

Jesus said he needed to be baptized to

"fulfil all righteousness" (Matthew 3:15).

Jesus went into the water and John baptized him by immersion, to show us the way.

#4 **Choose the Right by Praying to Heavenly Father as Jesus Did.**

♥ Jesus taught his disciples and others how to pray.
♥ He said personal prayers should be in secret.
♥ He said each prayer should be different, and not be full of *vain repetitions*.
♥ He taught us how to pray:
- BEGIN our prayers saying: Our Father in Heaven.
- THANK him for our blessings.
- ASK FOR BLESSINGS and help. Then,
-CLOSE OUR PRAYER in the name of Jesus Christ, Amen.

    Heavenly Father will answer prayers that are said in this way.
IF WE PRAY, HEAVENLY FATHER WILL BLESS US.

#5 **Choose the Right by Forgiving Others as Jesus Did.**

    Jesus said that if we have bad feelings about someone, we should forgive that person. If we do not forgive others, then we will not be forgiven by Heavenly Father.
    When Jesus was taken to Calvary and the people were crucifying him, he prayed to Heavenly Father and asked him to forgive them. Jesus said,
        "Father, forgive them; for they know not what they do" (Luke 23:34).
    Even though we have enemies, those who say bad things about us or treat us poorly, let's remember that even Jesus, who was crucified, asked Heavenly Father to forgive them, for they did not know what they were doing.

#6 **Choose the Right by Serving Others as Jesus Did.**

    Jesus wanted to serve his apostles. After the Last Supper, he poured water into a basin and washed their feet and wipe them with a towel.
    "Peter saith unto him, Thou shalt never wash my feet. Jesus answered him, If I wash thee not, thou hast no part with me. Simon Peter saith unto him, Lord, not my feet only, but also my hands and my head" (John 13:8-9).
    Washing the apostles' feet was one way Jesus could show them he loved them. Jesus said: *"Love one another; as I have loved you"* (John 13:34).
    How can we let our light shine? Say each day:

**BE BRIGHT--CHOOSE THE RIGHT--
JESUS IS OUR LIGHT**.

PATTERN: File Folder Show-and-Tell

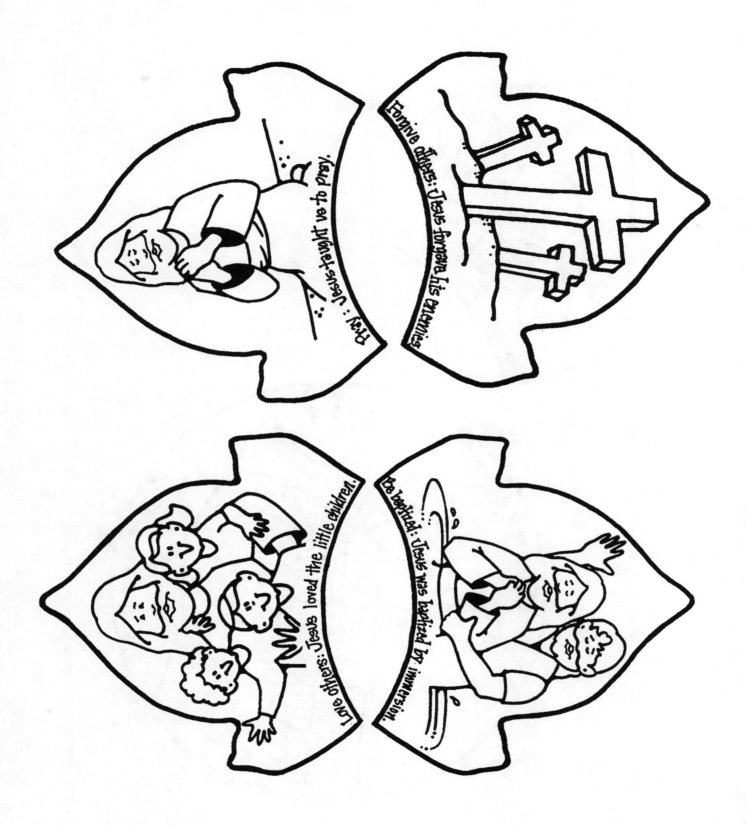

Side One of Sign

GAME: CHOOSE THE RIGHT: Red Light, Green Light

OBJECTIVE: Encourage family to think about choices. The way back to heaven is to follow the straight and narrow path. When temptation comes, they can STOP and CHOOSE THE RIGHT way.

TO MAKE GAME: Copy, color, and cut out CTR* and STOP signs (page 82). Glue signs back to back with a wooden craft stick or ruler in between signs.

TO PLAY GAME

1. <u>Positions</u>: Mark a line with a rope at one end of the room where a person known as Heaven's Helper stands behind the rope. Other players line up against the wall across the room facing the rope, 15-20 feet away.
2. <u>Players Follow Heaven's Helper</u>: Heaven's Helper turns his back on the players and points the CTR* sign toward other players across the room, saying, "Choose the Right." Players then advance toward Heaven's Helper, being careful to watch for directions.
3. <u>Stop Players</u>: Heaven's Helper yells "STOP" and turns around (STOP sign now faces players).
4. <u>Freeze</u>: When players hear STOP, they are to freeze in position. If Heaven's Helper catches them moving, he sends them back to start over.
5. <u>Winner</u>: The first person to cross over the rope into Heaven can be the leader or Heaven's Helper. Keep playing for 15 or 20 minutes. Then award a prize to each player. See prizes below.

PRIZE #1 "Souper" I Can Choose the Right (can with wisdom wordstrips).

1. Copy Choose the Right backward wordstrips and can label (pages 84-85).
2. Cut out wordstrips and place in can.
3. Cut out can label and glue it around an open clean soup can.
4. Take wordstrips out of the can and hold up to the light or read backwards in a mirror to learn ways they can Choose the Right.

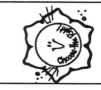

I Can Follow Jesus: I am beaming bright, as Jesus is my light.

PRIZE #2 Choose The Right: Jesus Is Our Light (light switch cover).

1. Copy light switch cover (page 85) on colored cardstock paper.
2. Color and cut out (including the center place for the light switch). Light switch reminds us that good choices make us happy.
3. Read message often:

> "Life can be a happy circle! The more you choose the right, the happier you become. The happier you become, the more your light shines."

*CTR is a registered trademark of The Church of Jesus Christ of Latter-day Saints.

PATTERN: CHOOSE THE RIGHT: Red Light, Green Light game (signs)

PATTERN: Prize (soup can label)

PRIZE #1
"Souper" I Can Choose the Right (can with wisdom wordstrips).

See page 81 for detailed instructions.

CHOOSE THE RIGHT
SOUP

I Can Choose the Right
Because Jesus Is My Light.
"When I sit in darkness, the LORD shall
be a light unto me." Micah 7:8

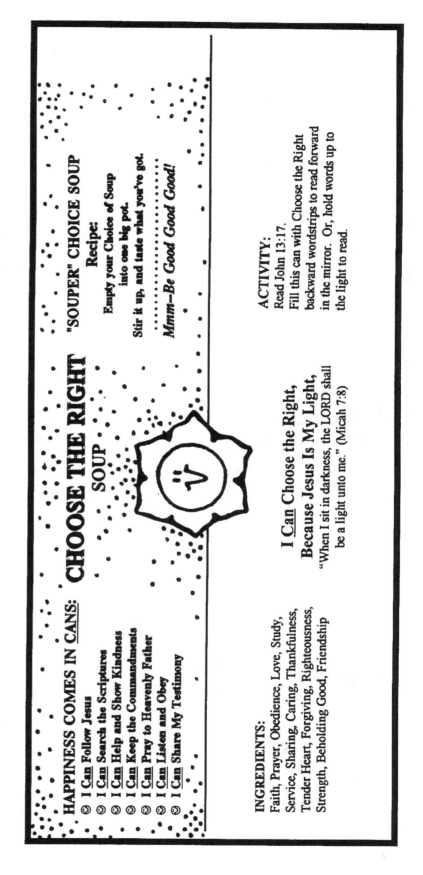

"SOUPER" CHOICE SOUP

Recipe:

Empty your Choice of Soup
into one big pot.

Stir it up, and taste what you've got.

Mmm—Be Good Good Good!

CHOOSE THE RIGHT
SOUP

HAPPINESS COMES IN CANS:

- I Can Follow Jesus
- I Can Search the Scriptures
- I Can Help and Show Kindness
- I Can Keep the Commandments
- I Can Pray to Heavenly Father
- I Can Listen and Obey
- I Can Share My Testimony

INGREDIENTS:
Faith, Prayer, Obedience, Love, Study,
Service, Sharing, Caring, Thankfulness,
Tender Heart, Forgiving, Righteousness,
Strength, Beholding Good, Friendship

I Can Choose the Right,
Because Jesus Is My Light,
"When I sit in darkness, the LORD shall
be a light unto me." (Micah 7:8)

ACTIVITY:
Read John 13:17.
Fill this can with Choose the Right
backward wordstrips to read forward
in the mirror. Or, hold words up to
the light to read.

PATTERN: Prizes: "Souper" I Can Choose The Right (wordstrips to place in soup can)

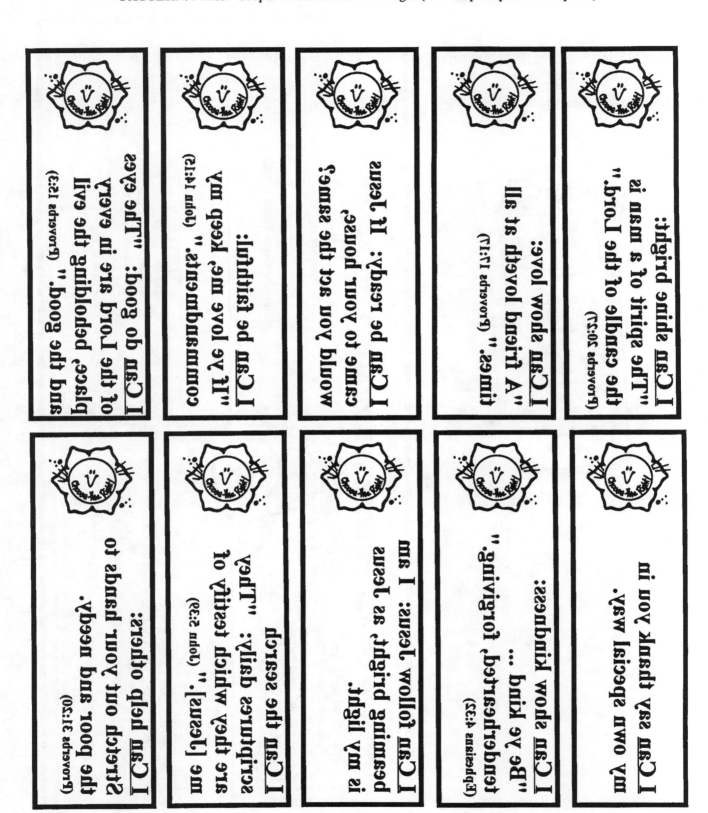

I Can do good: "The eyes of the Lord are in every place, beholding the evil and the good." (Proverbs 15:3)

I Can be faithful: "If ye love me, keep my commandments." (John 14:15)

I Can be ready: If Jesus came to your house, would you be the same?

I Can show love: "A friend loveth at all times." (Proverbs 17:17)

I Can shine bright: "The spirit of a man is the candle of the Lord." (Proverbs 20:27)

I Can help others: Stretch out your hands to the poor and needy. (Proverbs 31:20)

I Can search the scriptures: "They [scriptures] are they which testify of me [Jesus]." (John 5:39)

I Can follow Jesus: shining bright as Jesus, I am ... is my light.

I Can show kindness: "Be ye kind ... tenderhearted, forgiving ..." (Ephesians 4:32)

I Can thank you in your own special way.

PATTERN: Prizes: "Souper" I Can Choose the Right (wordstrips to place in soup can and light switch cover)

I Can listen to the still, small voice of the Holy Ghost.

I Can be strong: "The Lord is the strength of the way of the Lord is strength." (Proverbs 10:29)

I Can think about the right path: "Ponder the path of thy feet." (Proverbs 4:26)

I Can pray when I need to: "The Lord ... is far from the wicked: but he heareth the prayer of the righteous." (Proverbs 15:29)

I Can feel heaven closer

I Can keep the commandments: "Blessed are they that keep my ways." (Proverbs 8:32)

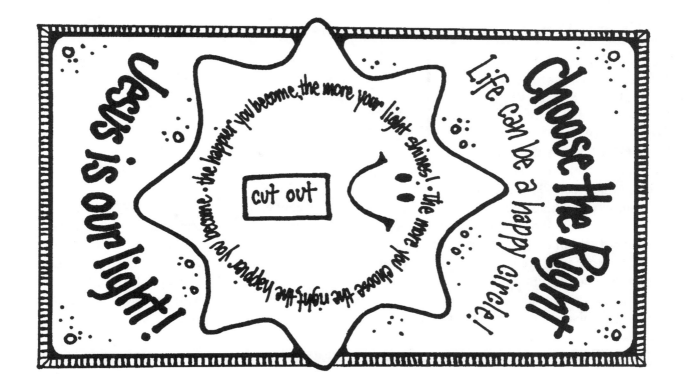

Choose the Right
Life can be a happy circle!

Jesus is our light!

the happier you become • the more your light shines! The more you choose the right, the happier you become

cut out

File Folder FAMILY HOME EVENING
CAPTAIN OF OUR SHIP: Jesus Is Our Life Savior

OPENING SONG: "I Feel My Savior's Love," page 74 in the *Children's Songbook*.*

INTRODUCTION:

Show a picture of Jesus and say: "Jesus is our LIFE SAVIOR: When sailing the sea of life, we can be protected against evil. Jesus is the captain of our ship. He is God's Son, and he knows his way back to our heavenly home.

"Jesus taught us how to live Heavenly Father's commandments. With his teachings we can keep our spiritual boat afloat.

"Jesus asked Heavenly Father to forgive us of our sins if we repent. Jesus died for us and was resurrected, so that we might live again. If we don't want to sink, let's follow the teachings of Jesus. He will bring us safely home.

"To sail the straight and narrow path, we need to follow the map found in the scriptures and listen to the latter day prophet. These will guide us through. Let's read the scriptures daily to stay on the lifeboat Jesus has provided."

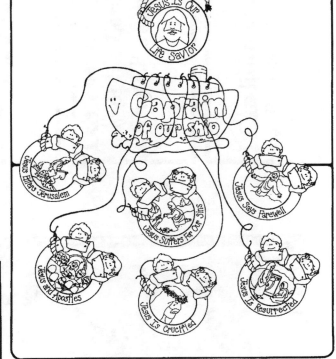

CAPTAIN OF OUR SHIP:
Jesus Is Our Life Savior
FILE FOLDER SHOW-AND-TELL:

CREATE: Cut out cue cards (pages 87-88) and file folder label (page iii). Color and cut out visuals (pages 89-91). Glue the label on file folder.

PRESENT: Read cue cards and place visuals on folder with tape or Velcro.

GAME: S.O.S. Save Our Ship: Jesus Is Our Life Savior (scripture reading and decision making). See rules on page 91.
TO MAKE GAME, copy and cut out cards (pages 92-97).
TO INTRODUCE GAME, say "Ahoy Mates! S.O.S. means danger is near; have faith, do not fear. This S.O.S. Save Our Ship activity will help you sail the sea of life. Jesus is the captain of our ship. Jesus is our life savior. He came to earth to save all of us from our sins. As you read about Jesus in the scriptures, you will learn how to keep your spiritual boat afloat. If we listen to him, we can keep our life in ship shape and make it through the storms. Let's learn how we can keep our spiritual boat afloat. **TO SET UP GAME**: Place 1 or 2 cards in a container at first so players will have a chance to read 1 or 2 of each card. Place all cards in container that are without scriptures or questions, e.g., Captain's Orders (shown above). If more time is allowed, increase the number of cards placed in the container. This activity can be continued for several weeks.

THOUGHT TREAT: <u>Jesus Is Our Life Savior shaped treats</u>. Serve doughnuts or Lifesavers or lifesaver shaped candies and ask family to share one thing they love about Jesus.

*Children's Songbook is published by The Church of Jesus Christ of Latter-day Saints, Salt Lake City, Utah.

#1

CAPTAIN OF OUR SHIP: Jesus Is Our Life Savior:

Jesus is our Life Savior. As we sail the sea of life, he is the captain of our ship. We can be protected against evil as we read the scriptures and learn of his teachings. We can sail safely to our heavenly home as we obey his commandments. He has shown us the way back.

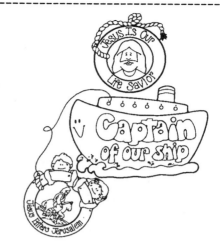

Jesus Enters Jerusalem, and Pharisees Plot to Kill Him:

The disciples of Jesus did not want him to go to Jerusalem. They knew that the chief priests and Pharisees wanted to kill him. As they entered Jerusalem, the people cried out, *"Blessed is the King of Israel that cometh in the name of the Lord"* (John 12:12-13*).*

Jesus wants us to have faith in him and know that his death was for a purpose. He had the power to save his own life, but he knew he had to go to Jerusalem to suffer, bleed, and die for us.

JESUS IS OUR LIFE SAVIOR.

#2

Jesus and Apostles: Sacrament and Last Supper: Jesus and his apostles
needed a place to eat the Passover dinner. Jesus sent Peter and John to look for a room. The Passover feast was to remind the Israelites that God saved them from Egyptian slavery with the help of Moses.

After the Passover feast, Jesus gave his apostles the first sacrament. He broke bread and blessed it. He told his apostles to eat this bread and always remember him, that he would die for them.

Jesus poured some wine into a cup and blessed it, and told the apostles to drink it and remember him. This was to remind them of the blood he would shed for them. He would bleed and suffer to take away the people's sins.

Jesus told them that wicked men would kill him. This made the apostles sad, for they loved Jesus. Jesus knew that Judas would tell the wicked men where he was. Judas was one of his apostles.

Jesus wants us to remember him each week as we partake of the sacrament. As we eat the bread, we are to remember that he allowed his body to be slain, and as we drink the water, we are to remember that his blood was shed. He suffered and died for our sins. The sacrament is very sacred and special.

#3

Jesus Suffers for Our Sins in the Garden of Gethsemane: Jesus and the
apostles went to the Garden of Gethsemane to pray. He asked Peter, James, and John to wait while he prayed. He prayed for a long time, and the apostles fell asleep.

While Jesus prayed, he suffered greatly for the sins of all the people in the world. He suffered for all those who lived before him and who would live after him.

He went back to Peter, James, and John several times and found them sleeping. He went back to pray again and again. He asked them to stay awake.

He continued to pray, and suffered so much that blood came out of his skin. He shook with sorrow for the sins of the world. An angel came to help Jesus through this.

When his suffering was finally over, he came back and found Peter, James, and John sleeping. He told them that wicked men were coming to kill him.

Jesus wants us to remember that he suffered for our sins. He wants us to live a righteous life. If we do sin, he wants us to repent, pray, and ask for forgiveness. Then he wants us to choose the right.

#4 **Jesus Is Crucified and He Forgives His Enemies:** Wicked men were sent by the Pharisees to take Jesus as a prisoner. They came into the garden with sticks and swords. Judas kissed Jesus to show the wicked men who Jesus was. The Pharisees paid him for finding Jesus.

The Pharisees took him to Pilate, the Roman leader in Jerusalem. Pilate told the Pharisees Jesus had done nothing wrong. The Pharisees demanded Jesus' crucifixion. Pilate did not want trouble with the Pharisees, so he let his soldiers crucify Jesus.

The soldiers took Jesus and beat him with whips, and made fun of him. They made a crown of thorns and pressed it down on his head, which made his head bleed. They took him to a hill near Jerusalem, laid him on a wooden cross, and nailed his hands and feet to the cross. Then they lifted up the cross, causing him great pain.

Jesus prayed that Heavenly Father would forgive the soldiers who crucified him, for they did not know he was the Savior. Jesus asked the apostle John to take care of his mother.

Jesus suffered for many hours, then he died. His spirit left his body. The sky became dark, and there was a great earthquake. The soldiers were afraid. One of the apostles took Jesus' body, wrapped it in cloth, and placed it in a tomb. A large rock was placed in front of the tomb.

#5 **Jesus Is Resurrected: He Is Our Life Savior:** After the body of Jesus was in the tomb three days, two angels came and moved the rock away. This was on a Sunday morning.

A friend of Jesus, Mary Magdalene, came to the tomb. She saw that the body of Jesus was gone. She ran to tell the apostles Peter and John. They came and saw the cloth that he was buried in. They then rushed home.

Mary stayed at the tomb, crying. As she looked in the tomb, she saw two angels. The angels asked her why she was crying. She told them someone had taken away the body of Jesus.

Mary turned around and saw Jesus standing there. She thought he was the gardener. Jesus said, *"Mary."* Then she knew he was Jesus. He asked her to go tell the apostles he had been resurrected. She ran and told the apostles, but they did not believe her.

Later, Jesus came to the apostles. They were afraid, thinking Jesus was dead. Jesus asked them why they were afraid. He ask them to touch his hands and feet and feel the nail prints. They could see that Jesus was resurrected. He was alive again. His body and spirit had come together. The apostles were happy to see Jesus. They ate fish and honey with him.

As Jesus was the first person to be resurrected, all other people will be resurrected, too.

#6 **Jesus Says Farewell and Sends the Holy Ghost:** After Jesus was resurrected, he stayed with the apostles 40 days. He taught them about his church, and asked them to teach the gospel to all the people.

He said that he would leave soon, but he would send a comforter to guide and help them. This comforter would be the Holy Ghost.

Then Jesus went to Heavenly Father. As the apostles watched him ascend up to heaven, two men came down in white clothes. They stood by the apostles, saying that Jesus would come back someday. When he did come back, he would come out of heaven.

The apostles were now the leaders of the church. Judas was dead, so there were only 11 apostles. They chose Matthias to be the 12th apostle. The apostles held the priesthood and continued to teach the people and heal the sick. They were missionaries. People believed the teachings about Jesus, and joined his church. They were called saints.

Jesus is our LIFE SAVIOR. He is the captain of our ship. If we are to sail safely to our heavenly home, we must do as he taught. Jesus wants us to follow in his steps--to pray often, read the scriptures, be baptized, be faithful members of his church, repent, learn of his miracles, live his parables, and teach others his gospel. This way we can live with Heavenly Father again.

S.O.S. Save Our Ship: Jesus Is Our Life Savior
HOW TO PLAY:

1. Mix cards (large and small) and stack in a pile together.
2. Divide into two teams and take turns drawing a card.
3. If you draw a large scripture card, read the card and scripture and add 10 points for your team.
4. If you draw a large Sunken Ship scripture card, read the card and subtract 10 points for your team.
5. If you draw a large Sink or Swim card, read the card and make a "sink" or "swim" choice and add 10 points.
6. If you draw a small card without any writing, you add 10 extra points, with the exception of the Sunken Ship card, where you subtract 10 points.
7. The team with the most points wins!

PATTERN: S.O.S. Save Our Ship: Jesus Is Our Life Savior game cards

Save Our Ship

S.O.S.
Save Our Ship

PRAY TO HEAVENLY FATHER.

"Whosoever shall call on the name of the Lord shall be saved."
Acts 2:21

add 10 Points

S.O.S.
Save Our Ship

KEEP GOING AND NEVER GIVE UP.

"He that endureth to the end shall be saved."
Matthew 10:22

add 10 Points

S.O.S.
Save Our Ship

FAITH WITHOUT WORKS IS DEAD.
"Ask in faith, nothing wavering. For he that wavereth is like a wave of the sea driven with the wind and tossed."
James 1:6

add 10 Points

S.O.S.
Save Our Ship

BE HAPPY THAT JESUS SAVED YOU FROM SPIRITUAL DEATH (if you choose the right).
"And my spirit hath rejoiced in God my Saviour." Luke 1:47

add 10 Points

S.O.S.
Save Our Ship

IF YOU REPENT AND CHOOSE THE RIGHT, YOU CAN BE SAVED.

"JESUS ... shall save his people from their sins." Matthew 1:21

add 10 Points

Captain's Orders

CAPTAIN'S ORDERS

· ·

SEEK HEAVENLY THINGS FIRST,
AND BLESSINGS WILL COME.

"Seek ye first the
kingdom of God,
and all his
righteousness; and
all these things shall
be added unto you."
Matthew 6:33

add 10 Points

CAPTAIN'S ORDERS

· ·

CHURCH, SCRIPTURES, SING, AND
PRAY--TO KEEP THE SABBATH DAY

"Remember the
sabbath day, to keep
it holy. Six days ... do
all thy work: But the
seventh day is the
sabbath of the Lord
thy God: in it thou
shalt not do any
work." Exodus 20:8-10

add 10 Points

CAPTAIN'S ORDERS

· ·

BELIEVE TO RECEIVE.
PRAY TO ASK.

"Therefore I say
unto you, What
things soever ye
desire, when ye
pray, believe that ye
receive them, and ye
shall have them."
Mark 11:24

add 10 Points

CAPTAIN'S ORDERS

· ·

TO EVERYONE, EVEN
BRANDEN, BETH, AND
BAILEY, ... READ THE
SCRIPTURES DAILY.

"It is written,
Man shall not live
by bread alone, but
by every word that
proceedeth out of
the mouth of God."

add 10 Points

CAPTAIN'S ORDERS

· ·

CHOOSE THE RIGHT
TO KEEP HEAVEN IN SIGHT.

"If ye love me,
keep my commandments.
And I will pray the Father,
and he shall give you
another Comforter [Holy
Ghost], that he may abide
with you forever."

John 14:15-16

add 10 Points

Heavenly Treasures

Heavenly Treasures

A DIM LIGHT IS A BURIED TREASURE; LET YOUR LIGHT SHINE.

"Ye are the light of the world. Let your light so shine before men, that they may see your good works, and glorify your Father which is in heaven."

Matthew 5:14, 16

add 10 Points

Heavenly Treasures

SEARCH THE SCRIPTURES TO FIND TREASURES FOR HEART AND MIND.

"He shall read therein all the days of his life: that he may learn to ... keep all his words ... to do them ... that he turn not ... from the commandment."

Deuteronomy 17:19-20

add 10 Points

Heavenly Treasures

AS YOU PRAY TO HEAVENLY FATHER, ASK FOR HEAVENLY TREASURES.

"Pray to thy Father which is in secret; and thy Father ... shall reward thee openly."

Matthew 6:6

add 10 Points

Heavenly Treasures

A TESTIMONY STARTS IN YOUR HEART AND SPREADS TO YOUR DEEDS.

"Not every one that saith unto me, Lord, Lord, shall enter into the kingdom of heaven; but he that doeth the will of my Father which is in heaven." Matthew 7:21

add 10 Points

Heavenly Treasures

WORK FOR RIGHTEOUS RICHES.

"Wealth gotten by vanity shall be diminished: but he that gathereth by labour shall increase."

Proverbs 13:11

add 10 Points

Sunken Ship

Sunken Ship

YOU WERE TOO SCARED TO BEAR YOUR TESTIMONY.

"For God hath not given us the spirit of fear, but of power, and of love, and of a sound mind."
2 Timothy 1:7

subtract 10 Points

Sunken Ship

YOU DIDN'T OBEY ALL OF GOD'S COMMANDMENTS.

"Put on the whole armour of God that ye may be able to stand against the wiles of the devil."
Ephesians 6:11

subtract 10 Points

Sunken Ship

YOU FORGOT TO FOLLOW JESUS.

"Follow me, and I will make you fishers of men [missionaries]. And they straightway left their nets, and followed him."
Matthew 4:19-20

subtract 10 Points

Sunken Ship

YOU BECAME WEAK. YOU FORGOT THAT THE SCRIPTURES GIVE YOU POWER.

"Jesus answered and said unto them, Ye do err, not knowing the scriptures, nor the power of God."
Matthew 22:29

subtract 10 Points

Sunken Ship

AHOY MATES! OBEDIENCE IS THE KEY TO HEAVEN'S GATES.

"Strive to enter in at the strait gate: for many, I say ... will seek to enter in, and shall not be able."
Luke 13:24

subtract 10 Points

Sink or Swim

Sink or Swim

It's the Sabbath day today, and you must decide whether to learn or play.

CHOOSE ONE:

Do you sink or swim?

☐ **SINK:** "Let's hit the pool," you say. "The sun is out and I want to stay cool."

☐ **SWIM:** You think in your mind you can swim any time, but today is the Lord's day and you will listen, learn, and obey.

add 10 Points

Sink or Swim

Your teacher asks you to stay after school. You wonder what is wrong.

CHOOSE ONE:

Do you sink or swim?

☐ **SINK:** Ditch class early, and all night worry.

☐ **SWIM:** Go see teacher.

add 10 Points

Sink or Swim

You have a problem, and the choice that is right is out of sight.

CHOOSE ONE:

Do you sink or swim?

☐ **SINK:** Ask your friends what you should do.

☐ **SWIM:** Write the problem on paper. Ask Heavenly Father to help you. Then listen to your heart for the answer.

add 10 Points

Sink or Swim

You have a math test and haven't studied. You're afraid, if you don't pass, you'll be grounded in class.

CHOOSE ONE:

Do you sink or swim?

☐ **SINK:** Coax your friend into sharing his brains. Ooops, the teacher saw you.

☐ **SWIM:** Tell your teacher that you'll have to pass, and you'll study harder in class.

add 10 Points

Sink or Swim

Your friends tell you it's the only way to go. They tempt you to smoke.

CHOOSE ONE:

Do you sink or swim?

☐ **SINK:** Try the cigarette and choke.

☐ **SWIM:** Tell your friends you'd rather go without, even if they pout.

add 10 Points

Sink or Swim

Sink or Swim

It's your father's birthday on Sunday, and you forgot to buy a gift.

CHOOSE ONE:

Do you sink or swim?

☐ **SINK:** You go to the store on Sunday and buy your dad a brand new tie.

☐ **SWIM:** You know that Sunday is not the day to shop, and you say, "Dad, I'm sorry, I forgot. If it's okay, I'll get your gift another day."

add 10 Points

Sink or Swim

Each day you say, "It's time to pray."

CHOOSE ONE:

Do you sink or swim?

☐ **SINK:** You forget to kneel and talk to Heavenly Father, who is so real.

☐ **SWIM:** You kneel each day to Heavenly Father and pray. You give your thanks and repent of pranks. You ask him to bless you and guide you to choose the right.

add 10 Points

Sink or Swim

Your parents are always on the run, and don't have time for fun.

CHOOSE ONE:

Do you sink or swim?

☐ **SINK:** Clam up when your parents are around, and forget their rules when they are out of town.

☐ **SWIM:** Make a plan and show them fun ways to be

add 10 Points

Sink or Swim

Some days are crazy. There's so much work to do.

CHOOSE ONE:

Do you sink or swim?

☐ **SINK:** Say, "Work?" "I don't want to." Then join the couch potato crew.

☐ **SWIM:** Say, "I'm Johnny on the spot. Afraid of work I'm not."

add 10 Points

Sink or Swim

Money is a problem. I never have enough. Wish it grew on trees, that nice green stuff. **CHOOSE ONE:**

Do you sink or swim?

☐ **SINK:** I wait around for birthdays, Christmas and the like. I make my list and wish for things out of sight!

☐ **SWIM:** I don't depend on Mom or Dad to buy the things I wish I had. I make a list of others' needs, and plan to give, not just receive.

add 10 Points

File Folder FAMILY HOME EVENING

IN HIS STEPS: Spotlighting the Life of Jesus

SONG: "I'm Trying to Be Like Jesus," page 78 in the *Children's Songbook**.

INTRODUCTION: Show a picture of Jesus and say: "The pathway to follow is clear. The path that leads back to our Heavenly Father and Jesus is recorded in the scriptures. We can find the truth and the light. We can find the joy that comes from walking in the steps of Jesus. Let's learn of the places he walked, the people he healed, the heartwarming stories he told. Let's learn to love as he did."

IN HIS STEPS:
Spotlighting the
Life of Jesus
FILE FOLDER
SHOW-AND-TELL:

CREATE: Cut out cue cards (pages 99-100) and file folder label (page iii). Color and cut out visuals (pages 101-102). Glue the label on file folder.
PRESENT: Read cue cards and place visuals on folder with tape or Velcro.

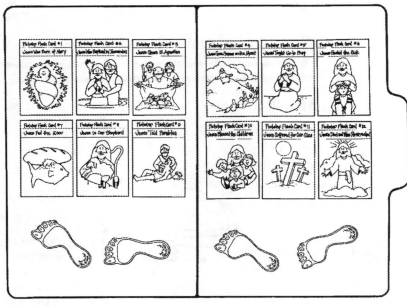

ACTIVITY:
SEARCH, PONDER, and PLAY: The New Testament Game—Spotlighting the Life of Jesus. See page 103 for details.

THOUGHT
TREAT: Footstep Sugar Cookies. Detailed on page 114.

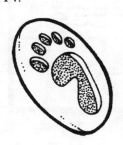

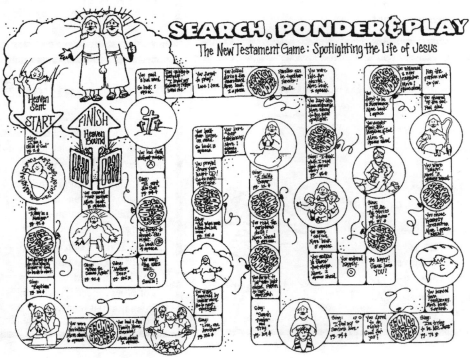

Children's Songbook is published by The Church of Jesus Christ of Latter-day Saints, Salt Lake City, Utah.

FILE FOLDER SHOW-AND-TELL

#1   **IN HIS STEPS: Spotlighting the Life of Jesus**
. . . . (SHOW FOOTPRINTS)
         Let's follow in the footsteps of Jesus.
Let's spotlight his life.

FOOTSTEP FLASH CARD #1
Jesus Was Born of Mary in Bethlehem.
He is the Son of God, our Heavenly Father.

FOOTSTEP FLASH CARD #2
Jesus was baptized by immersion in the River Jordan by John
the Baptist.

#2   FOOTSTEP FLASH CARD #3
         Jesus Chose 12 Apostles:
         Some were fishermen. "Jesus said unto them,
Come ye after me, and I will make you ... fishers of men."
He wanted them to give up their fishing and go teach the
gospel to men--to be missionaries (Mark 1:17).

FOOTSTEP FLASH CARD #4
Jesus Gave Sermon on the Mount: Many people
gathered near a mountainside to hear him. He told the
people how to be happy and how to get back to heaven.
Some teachings were called the Beatitudes. One
Beatitude is: "Blessed are the pure in heart for they shall
see God" (Matthew 5:8).

#3   FOOTSTEP FLASH CARD #5
         Jesus Taught Us to Pray:
         Jesus told the people how to pray to Heavenly
Father. He told us to pray in secret and that our prayers
should not be shouted.

FOOTSTEP FLASH CARD #6
Jesus Healed the Sick:
Jesus healed a woman who was sick. She touched his robe,
and her faith made her well. He healed a blind man, cast
out devils, healed the lepers, and raised a man and a girl
from the dead with his priesthood power.

FILE FOLDER SHOW-AND-TELL

#4 FOOTSTEP FLASH CARD #7
Jesus Fed Five Thousand:
Many people came to Galilee to hear Jesus. He taught them all day, until night. They had not eaten. Jesus did not want to send them away to get food. He wanted them to stay so he could continue to teach them. He only had five loaves of bread and two fishes. With the priesthood, he blessed what little food they had and fed five thousand people.

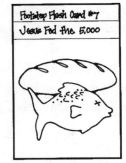

FOOTSTEP FLASH CARD #8
Jesus Is Our Shepherd:
Jesus said a good shepherd feeds and takes care of his sheep. He told a parable of a shepherd who lost a lamb. The shepherd searched and searched until he finally found it. A good shepherd would give up his life to save his sheep. Jesus was a good shepherd. He gave up his life to save us from our sins.

#5 FOOTSTEP FLASH CARD #9
Jesus Told Parables:
Jesus taught the people with stories. One great story was of the Good Samaritan. There was a Jew who was robbed and left alongside the road. Several men passed him by. But one good Samaritan man stopped and took care of him.

FOOTSTEP FLASH CARD #10
Jesus Blessed the Children:
People wanted Jesus to see their children. The disciples said, "No," Jesus was too busy. Jesus asked the disciples to bring the children to him. He loved the little children. He told the disciples and the people that if they wanted to live with Heavenly Father, they were to become like little children and believe in him.

#6 FOOTSTEP FLASH CARD #11
Jesus Suffered for Our Sins:
Jesus prayed in the Garden of Gethsemane. He asked Heavenly Father to forgive all of us for what we do wrong. He prayed so hard that he sweat blood. He was in great pain in body and spirit for the wrongdoings of all people who would ever live.

FOOTSTEP FLASH CARD #12
Jesus Died and Was Resurrected: Some wicked men took Jesus and crucified him. They nailed his hands and feet to a cross where he died. He came back to life three days later and showed the nail prints in his hands and feet to his apostles. Jesus lived again, and so can we. We can follow IN HIS STEPS.

ACTIVITY: SEARCH, PONDER, and PLAY: The New Testament Game—
Spotlighting the Life of Jesus

OBJECTIVE: You were Heaven Sent and Heaven Bound. This game will show you where Jesus walked and what he did to show us the way back to heaven. We can follow in his steps as we search, ponder, and pray about what we learn.

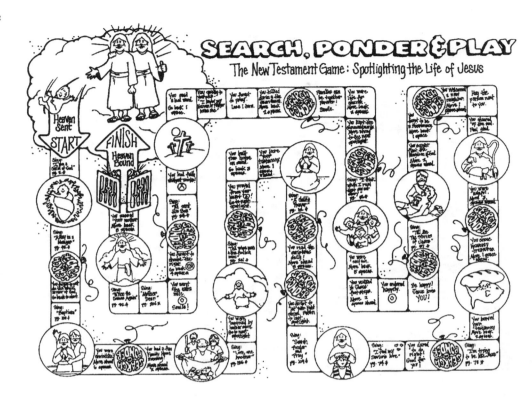

TO SET UP GAME:
1. Cut out the four part game board (pages 104-107) and glue to the back of two file folders taped together.
2. Cut out Footstep Flash Cards #1-12 (used for the SHOW-AND-TELL presentation).
3. Cut out foot markers and "MOVE" numbers (page 108), placing numbers in a container to draw from.
4. Cut out the 12 SEARCH and PONDER cards (pages 109-110). Lay cards face up in two piles (SEARCH and PONDER).

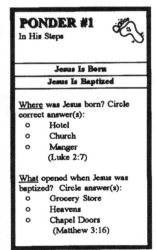

SEARCH #1
In His Steps

| Jesus Is Born |
| Jesus Is Baptized |

"And she brought forth her firstborn son, and wrapped him in swaddling clothes, and laid him in a _ _ _ _ _ _ _ ; because there was no room for them in the inn." (Luke 2:7)

. . . .

"And Jesus, when he was baptized, went up straightway out of the _ _ _ _ _ _: and, lo, the heavens were opened unto him." (Matthew 3:16)

PONDER #1
In His Steps

| Jesus Is Born |
| Jesus Is Baptized |

<u>Where</u> was Jesus born? Circle correct answer(s):
o   Hotel
o   Church
o   Manger
      (Luke 2:7)

<u>What</u> opened when Jesus was baptized? Circle answer(s):
o   Grocery Store
o   Heavens
o   Chapel Doors
      (Matthew 3:16)

TO PLAY GAME: (1) Divide into two teams or play individually, placing a foot marker on START for each team or individual. (2) Team or player draws a "MOVE" number from a container and moves on the board the number of spaces. (3) If you land on <u>SEARCH OR PONDER</u>, draw a SEARCH or a PONDER card. Look up the scripture to fill in the missing words or answer the question, reading aloud. (4) If you land on a <u>spotlight circle</u> draw a footstep flash card and tell what you know about the event in Jesus' life shown on the flash card. (5) If you land on a "sing" space, sing the song from the *Children's Songbook*.

RULES: If you are sent back to the START, you only have to go back once. To speed up the game, skip spaces where other players are.

Footstep Flash Card #1
Jesus Was Born of Mary

OH, PONDER & PLAY

Testament Game: Spotlighting the Life of Jesus

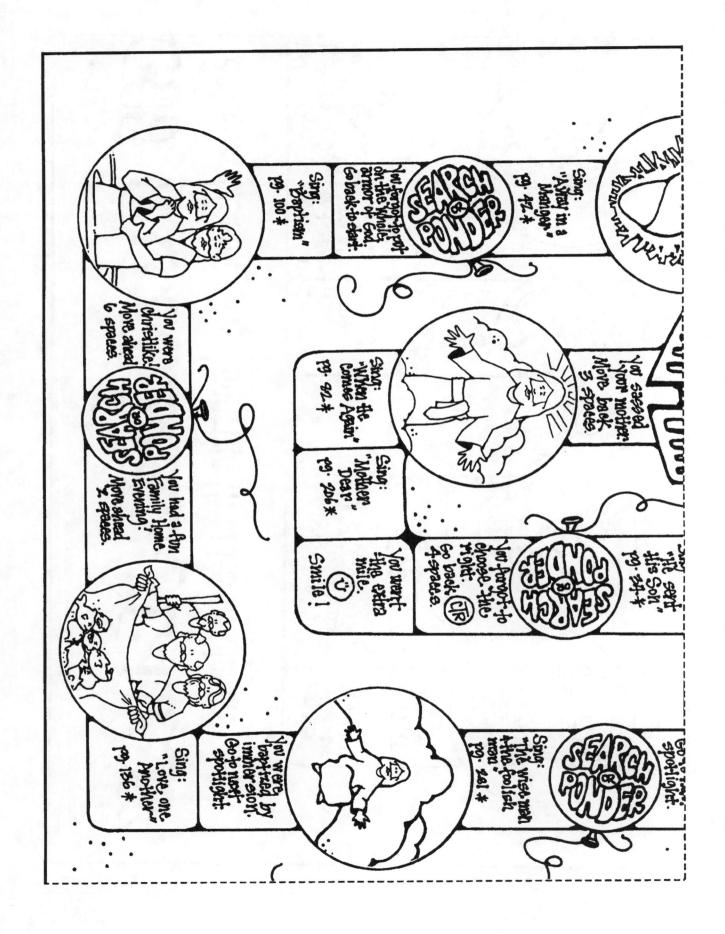

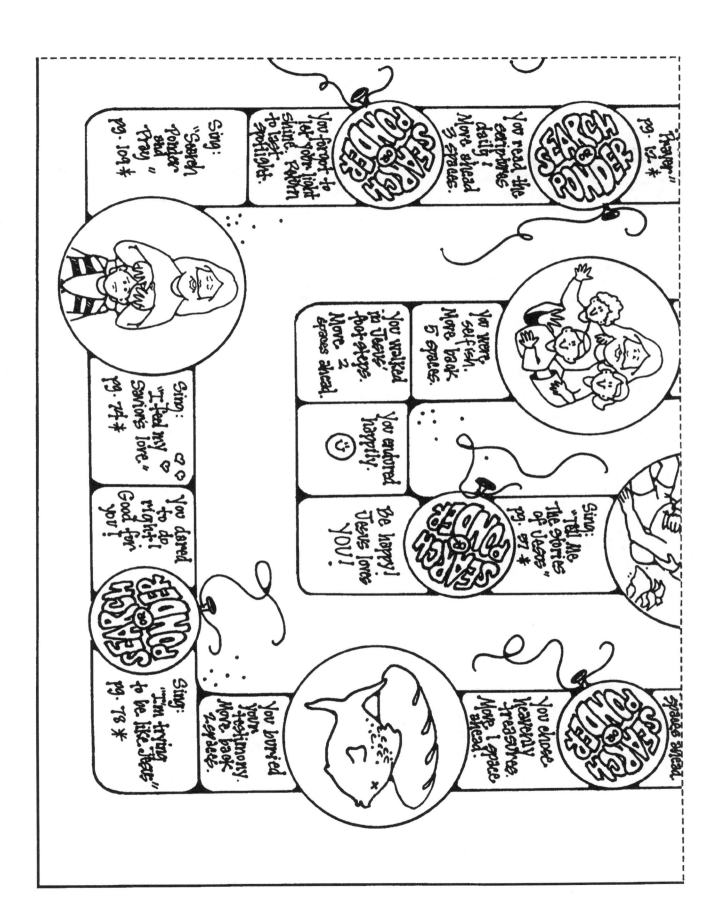

In His Steps:
Spotlighting the Life of Jesus
File Folder FAMILY HOME EVENINGS

PLACE LABEL ON FILE FOLDER TAB

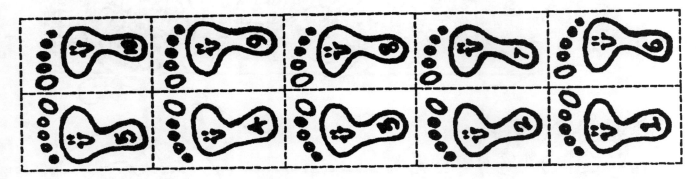

MOVE 1	MOVE 2	MOVE 3	MOVE 4	MOVE 5
MOVE 1	MOVE 2	MOVE 3	MOVE 4	MOVE 5
MOVE 1	MOVE 2	MOVE 3	MOVE 4	MOVE 5
MOVE 1	MOVE 2	MOVE 3	MOVE 4	MOVE 5
MOVE 1	MOVE 2	MOVE 3	MOVE 4	MOVE 5
MOVE 1	MOVE 2	MOVE 3	MOVE 4	MOVE 5
MOVE 1	MOVE 2	MOVE 3	MOVE 4	MOVE 5
MOVE 1	MOVE 2	MOVE 3	MOVE 4	MOVE 5
MOVE 1	MOVE 2	MOVE 3	MOVE 4	MOVE 5
MOVE 1	MOVE 2	MOVE 3	MOVE 4	MOVE 5
MOVE 1	MOVE 2	MOVE 3	MOVE 4	MOVE 5
MOVE 1	MOVE 2	MOVE 3	MOVE 4	MOVE 5
MOVE 1	MOVE 2	MOVE 3	MOVE 4	MOVE 5
MOVE 1	MOVE 2	MOVE 3	MOVE 4	MOVE 5
MOVE 1	MOVE 2	MOVE 3	MOVE 4	MOVE 5
MOVE 1	MOVE 2	MOVE 3	MOVE 4	MOVE 5
MOVE 1	MOVE 2	MOVE 3	MOVE 4	MOVE 5
MOVE 1	MOVE 2	MOVE 3	MOVE 4	MOVE 5

SEARCH CARDS

SEARCH #1
In His Steps

Jesus Is Born
Jesus Is Baptized

"And she brought forth her firstborn son, and wrapped him in swaddling clothes, and laid him in a _ _ _ _ _ _ _; because there was no room for them in the inn." (Luke 2:7)

. . . .

"And Jesus, when he was baptized, went up straightway out of the _ _ _ _ _ _: and, lo, the heavens were opened unto him." (Matthew 3:16)

SEARCH #2
In His Steps

Jesus Chooses 12 Apostles
Sermon on the Mount

"And when it was day, he called unto him his

_ _ _ _ _ _ _ _ _ _: and of them he chose twelve, whom also he named apostles." (Luke 6:13)

. . . .

"And he opened his _ _ _ _ _ _, and taught them, saying, ... "Blessed are the pure in heart: for they shall see God." (Matthew 5:2 and 8)

SEARCH #3
In His Steps

Jesus Taught Us to Pray
Jesus Healed the Sick

"When thou prayest, enter into thy _ _ _ _ _ _ _, and when thou hast shut thy door, pray to thy _ _ _ _ _ _ _ which is in secret; and thy Father ... shall reward thee openly."   (Matthew 6:6)

A woman touched Jesus' robe: "And he said unto her, Daughter, thy faith hath made thee whole; go in peace, and be whole in thy _ _ _ _ _ _ _." (Mark 5:34)

SEARCH #4
In His Steps

Jesus Fed the 5,000
Jesus Is Our Shepherd

"And when he had taken the five loaves and the two fishes, he looked to heaven, and _ _ _ _ _ _ _ _, and brake the loaves, and gave them to his disciples to set before them; and the two fishes divided he among them all." (Mark 6:41)

. . . .

"I am the good shepherd: the good shepherd giveth his _ _ _ _ _ for the sheep." (John 10:11)

SEARCH #5
In His Steps

Jesus Told Parables
Jesus Blessed the Children

- Parable of Good Samaritan -
"A certain man ... fell among thieves which ...

_ _ _ _ _ _ _ _ him and departed." (Luke 10:30)
"But a certain Samaritan ... had compassion on him." (Luke 10:33)

. . . .

Jesus said, "Suffer the little children to come unto me, and _ _ _ _ _ _ them not: for of such is the kingdom of God." (Mark 10:14)

SEARCH #6
In His Steps

Jesus Suffered for Our Sins
Jesus Died and Was Resurrected

"And he ... prayed, saying, O my Father, if it be possible, let this _ _ _ _ pass from me: nevertheless not as I will, but as thou wilt." (Matthew 26:39)

. . . .

"And when they were come to the place, which is called Calvary, there they

_ _ _ _ _ _ _ _ him." (Luke 23:33)
"It behoved Christ to suffer, and to _ _ _ _ from the dead the third day." (Luke 24:46)

PONDER CARDS

PONDER #1
In His Steps

Jesus Is Born
Jesus Is Baptized

<u>Where</u> was Jesus born? Circle the correct answer(s):
- o   Hotel
- o   Church
- o   Manger

(Luke 2:7)

<u>What</u> opened when Jesus was baptized? Circle answer(s):
- o   Grocery Store
- o   Heavens
- o   Chapel Doors

(Matthew 3:16)

PONDER #2
In His Steps

Jesus Chooses 12 Apostles
Sermon on the Mount

What is another name for Jesus' apostles? (Luke 6:13)

_ _ _ _ _ _ _ _ _ _

What did Jesus say you have need to hunger and thirst after?

(Matthew 5:6)

_ _ _ _ _ -

_ _ _ _ _ _ _ _

PONDER #3
In His Steps

Jesus Taught Us to Pray
Jesus Healed the Sick

Should we pray in the streets for all to hear, or should we pray in

_ _ _ _ _ _ _ ?

(Matthew 6:6)

What was the woman healed of when she touched Jesus' robe?

(Mark 5:34)

_ _ _ _ _ _

PONDER #4
In His Steps

Jesus Fed the 5,000
Jesus Is Our Shepherd

How did Jesus turn five loaves of bread and two fish into food enough to feed 5,000 hungry people? (Mark 6:41)

Jesus _ _ _ _ _ _ _
the food.

What does a "good shepherd" do for his sheep? (John 10:11)

A good shepherd gives up his
_ _ _ _ _ to protect his sheep.

PONDER #5
In His Steps

Jesus Told Parables
Jesus Blessed the Children

What does the word "compassion" mean? (Luke 10:33)
Look up the word in a dictionary.
Write the definition below.
Compassion means:

_____

_____

What kingdom are you from?

(Mark 10:14)
Jesus said the children are of the kingdom of _ _ _.

PONDER #6
In His Steps

Jesus Suffered for Our Sins
Jesus Died and Was Resurrected

As Jesus prayed in the Garden of Gethsemane, what was one thing he prayed for? (Matthew 26:39)

"Let this _ _ _ pass from me." Means: let this suffering pass.

After Jesus died, how many days passed before he came to life again? (Luke 24:46)

_____ days passed

I ❤ Family Home Evening THOUGHT TREAT:
Heavenly Treasures: Follow the Straight and Narrow Path

**MILK SHAKE with Heaven Sent,
Heaven Bound straw decoration**

TO MAKE: "Moo"-ve into the kitchen freezer, take out your favorite ice cream, and fill the blender 3/4ths full. Then add milk and blend until creamy smooth. Make the Heaven Sent straw decoration (page 115), paper punch it and slip it over a straw.

ACTIVITY: As you sip, read John 3:12 and say, "I am Heaven Sent and Heaven Bound."

I ❤ Family Home Evening THOUGHT TREAT:
Seeds of Faith: My Testimony is Growing

Seeds of Faith Watermelon Cookies
TO MAKE: (1) Color sugar cookie dough (recipe right) with red food coloring. (2) Roll dough and cut into round shapes; then cut in half.(1) Color sugar cookie dough (recipe right) with red food coloring. (2) Roll dough and cut into round shapes; then cut in half. (3) Bake cookies 8-9 minutes at 350° degrees. (4) Divide white frosting and color with food coloring: 3/4 red and 1/4 green. Frost each cookie with red frosting, and trim in green for melon rind. (5) Place miniature chocolate chips on top for seeds. **ACTIVITY:** As you eat cookies, read Matthew 17:20 and say, "The New Testament and other scriptures are seeds of faith that increase my testimony of Jesus."

*SUGAR COOKIE DOUGH: 1 cup (2 sticks) butter, 1 1/4 cup sugar, 1 teaspoon vanilla, 1 teaspoon cream of tartar, 2 eggs, 3 1/2 cups flour, 1 teaspoon soda. Cream together. Add 1/4 cup flour if needed.
EASY ROLL OUT: Place dough between two sheets of waxed paper.

I ❤ Family Home Evening THOUGHT TREAT:
Angel Tells of Two Births: John and Jesus

ANGEL FOOD CAKE & BABY LOVE MILK
TO MAKE: Copy signs (page 116) on light blue paper. Frost an angel food cake with frosting mixed with whipping cream colored with two drops of blue food coloring. Top with coconut and sign. Tape Baby Love Milk labels to 8-ounce cups. Fill with milk. **ACTIVITY:** As you eat, read Luke 1:13, 30-32, 39-42 and say, "We love babies, and we love John and Jesus. Gabriel was the angel who came to tell Mary and Elisabeth the good news!"

I ❤ Family Home Evening THOUGHT TREAT:
Create Me: I'm Trying to Be Like Jesus

Balanced Life Graham Cracker Sandwiches

TO MAKE: Break a graham cracker in half. Frost the center and top. Frost the center and top. Place four gum drops on top. Draw strings with frosting as if gumdrops were balloons.
ACTIVITY: Read Luke 2:52, and tell family that these gumdrop balloons remind us of the four areas in which Jesus balanced his life: mental, physical, spiritual, and social. Set goals in these areas to become like Jesus.

I ❤ Family Home Evening THOUGHT TREAT:
Fishers of Men: Jesus Chose 12 Apostles

Jiggly Jelly Fish Pond. Make this fun Jello pond with fish afloat.
POND: Two 6-ounce packages of blue or green Jello. **FISH:** Two different colors, 6 ounces each, of yellow, red, or orange Jello. **FISH POND:** Make firm Jello recipe, which requires two 6-ounce packages of blue or green Jello and water (follow package directions). Pour hot Jello into a 13 x 9-inch pan. Chill three hours or until firm.
JIGGLY JELLY FISH: Make firm Jello recipe above, dividing water portion in half for each 6-ounce package to make firm fish of different colors. Pour hot Jello into two individual cake or pie pans to set (refrigerate) 2 hours or until firm. Run warm water over bottom of pan and release Jello onto waxed paper. Cut into fish shapes with knife. Place fish on top of Jello pond. **ACTIVITY:** Read Matthew 4:17-20.

I ❤ Family Home Evening THOUGHT TREAT:
Blessed Beatitudes: Jesus Gave the Sermon on the Mount

Honey Buzz Taffy

Honey reminds us that heaven is sweet. Jesus gave us the beatitudes to show us the sweetest way to heaven. Recipe makes 35 pieces of taffy. You'll need 1 cup honey and some waxed paper.
TO MAKE: Heat honey to boil stage and cook on medium heat 7-10 minutes, stirring often. Test for crackle stage. Drop ½ teaspoon of boiling honey into ½ cup of cold water. If medium ball forms, it's done. Butter a surface and pour honey onto surface to cool 3 minutes. Pull taffy with buttered fingers until light and porous. Cut into pieces and wrap with waxed paper.

I ❤ Family Home Evening THOUGHT TREAT:
Blessed Beatitudes: Jesus Gave Sermon on the Mount

"Bee"-atitude Bagles

TO MAKE: Cut bagel in half and spread a bagel in half and spread a mixture of 1/2 cream cheese and 1/2 honey on top. Cut out the "'Bee' a buzzy bee-atitude believer!" sign (page 117). Insert a toothpick into two dots and insert signs into bagels.

ACTIVITY: Read Matthew 5:1-12 to review the

I ❤ Family Home Evening THOUGHT TREAT:
Gifts He Gave: Tell Me the Stories of Jesus

Unforgettable Parable Cupcakes

TO MAKE: Write the scripture reference for the following parables on wordstrips and bake (wrapped in aluminum foil) inside cupcakes. Copy and place the elephant tag (page 117) on top of two or more cupcakes (shown right).

ACTIVITY: As you eat the cupcake find the parable (scripture). Then read the parable and tell your family in your own words. Parable Scriptures: The Lost Sheep (Luke 15:4-5), The Talents (Matthew 25:14-18), Ten Young Women (Matthew 25:1-4, 8, 10), The Lost Son (Luke 15:11-14, 21-24), The Mustard Seed (Matthew 13:31-32), The Good Samaritan (Luke 10:30-34).

I ❤ Family Home Evening THOUGHT TREAT:
Gifts He Gave: Tell Me the Stories of Jesus

Gift Cookie

TO MAKE: Make oatmeal cookies, cool, wrap in clear plastic wrap or insert into a plastic bag. Tie a yarn or ribbon bow on the cookie to look like a gift.

ACTIVITY: Tell children that we should always remember the gifts Jesus gave when he told us his stories or parables. As children untie bow, ask them to tie this piece of yarn on their finger. When you tie a piece of yarn on your finger it helps you remember something important. Think of a parable you want to remember, read it in the scriptures, and then tell it to someone in your own words. Then you can take the string off your finger. Family members can tell someone a parable before going to bed.

I ❤ Family Home Evening THOUGHT TREAT:
Service with a Smile: Jesus Performed Miracles

"Chip" in and Help! Potato Chips

TO MAKE: Place label (page 118) and potato chips in a bag to remind family to "Chip in and help! Reach in, grab a chip, and 'chews' someone to help!" **ACTIVITY:** Read John 13:34. Then, as you are eating your bag of potato chips, talk about ways you might help one another, starting with each family member. Ask each family member to tell things they need help with. Then assign certain individuals to "chip" in and help.

I ❤ Family Home Evening THOUGHT TREAT:
Choose the Right: Jesus Is Our Light

Choo Choose the Right Soda Cracker Train

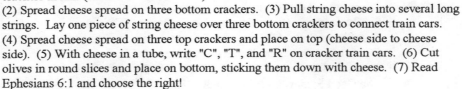

You'll Need: Soda crackers, cheese spread, string cheese, cheese in a tube, and olives (for wheels). One train serves three (one car each). Place cars together. To eat, cut between strings.
To Make Train Cars: (1) Break soda crackers in half (six halves for one train). (2) Spread cheese spread on three bottom crackers. (3) Pull string cheese into several long strings. Lay one piece of string cheese over three bottom crackers to connect train cars. (4) Spread cheese spread on three top crackers and place on top (cheese side to cheese side). (5) With cheese in a tube, write "C", "T", and "R" on cracker train cars. (6) Cut olives in round slices and place on bottom, sticking them down with cheese. (7) Read Ephesians 6:1 and choose the right!

I ❤ Family Home Evening THOUGHT TREAT:
In His Steps: Spotlighting the Life of Jesus

Footstep Sugar Cookies

TO MAKE: Footstep Sugar Cookies. Roll sugar cookie dough into 2-inch balls. Press half-way down. Make footprint with your fist, and toes with your fingers. Sprinkle foot impression with colored sugar. Bake at 350° for 8-10 minutes.

SUGAR COOKIE DOUGH:
1 cup (2 sticks) butter, 1 1/4 cup sugar, 1 teaspoon vanilla, 1 teaspoon cream of tartar, 1 teaspoon soda, 2 eggs, and 3 1/2 cups flour. Cream together.

ACTIVITY: As you eat footstep cookies, read John 13:15, 34 and say, "Let's walk in the steps of Jesus."

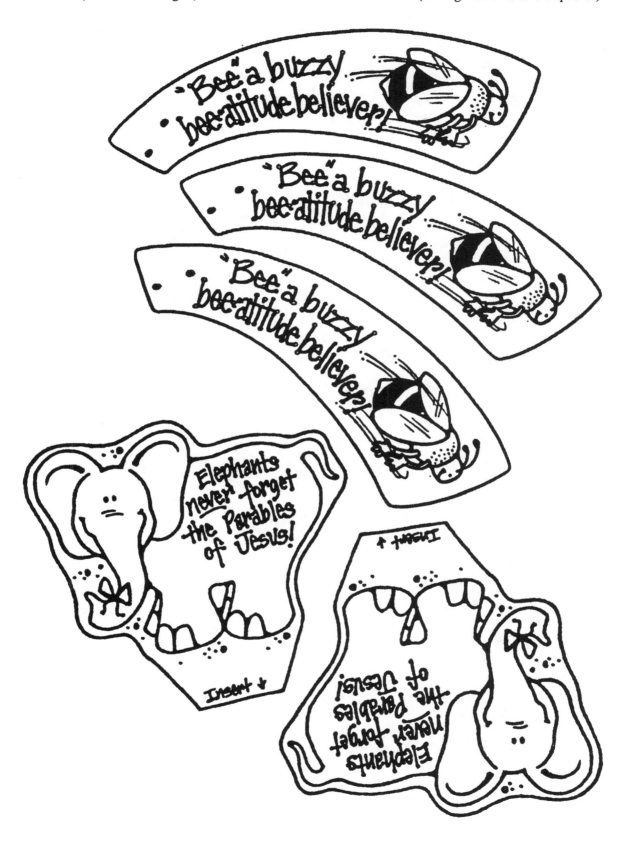

Home-spun Fun FAMILY HOME EVENINGS

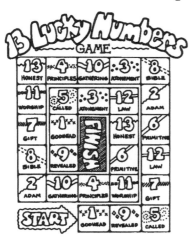

Build testimonies with the Articles of Faith 13 Lucky Numbers game.

Tired of those one-size-fits-all family home evening manuals, where the lesson and activities never quite seem to match the ages and stages of your children? Well, your problems are over! In this action-packed, fun-filled volume of fabulous lessons, games, activities, and treats, you'll find something for everyone, no matter what their age!

Whether your family has young children, grade school youngsters, teenagers, or a combination, you'll find age-appropriate games and activities for each of them in virtually every section.

Using the dozens of great lesson and activities in this book, you'll be able to help your children learn and understand basic gospel principles. And you can make each lesson as simple or elaborate as you wish.

You'll find these and more activities to make learning fun:
♥ "Bee"atitude cross match
♥ Child of God paper dolls
♥ Faith is Cool! glasses
♥ Faith-ful Saints guessing game
♥ Forgiving Faces flip chart
♥ Puzzled About Prayer crossword
♥ Priesthood Heals band-aid bandelo
♥ Sabbath Day Drama or Draw
♥ Sacrament manners match game
♥ Bear Testimony secret message
♥ Tithing origami purse/wallet
♥ Word of Wisdom voting ballot
♥ Baptism Promises poster

Mary H. Ross, Author and
Jennette Guymon-King, Illustrator
are the creators of

PRIMARY PARTNERS: *Lesson Activities to Make Learning Fun for:*
Nursery and Age 3 (Sunbeams)—Vol. 1 and II
CTR A and CTR B Ages 4-7
Book of Mormon Ages 8-11
Doctrine & Covenants/Church History Ages 8-11
Old Testament Ages 8-11
New Testament Ages 8-11 + CD-ROM
Achievement Days, Girls Ages 8-11
Many PRIMARY PARTNERS *on CD-ROM*

FAMILY HOME EVENING BOOKS:
Home-spun Fun FAMILY HOME EVENINGS
File Folder FAMILY HOME EVENINGS + CD-ROM

YOUNG WOMEN BOOKS:
Young Women Fun-tastic! Activities - Manual 3

MARY H. ROSS, *Author*
Mary Ross is an energetic mother, Primary
teacher, and has been an Achievement Days
leader. She loves to help children have a good
time while they learn. She has studied acting,
modeling, and voice. Her varied interests
include writing, creating activities and
children's parties, and cooking. Mary and her
husband, Paul, live with their daughter,
Jennifer, in Sandy, Utah

Photos by Scott Hancock, Provo, Utah

JENNETTE GUYMON-KING,
Illustrator
Jennette Guymon-King has studied graphic
arts and illustration at Utah Valley State
College and the University of Utah. She is
currently employed with a commercial
construction company. She served a mission
to Japan. Jennette enjoys sports, reading,
cooking, art, gardening, and freelance
illustrating. Jennette and her husband,
Clayton, live in Riverton, Utah.